THE WEAKEST LINK
QUIZ BOOK 2

THE WEAKEST LINK
QUIZ BOOK 2

PENGUIN BOOKS

793.73

Published by the Penguin Group
Penguin Books Ltd, 27 Wrights Lane, London W8 5TZ, England
Penguin Putnam Inc., 375 Hudson Street, New York, New York 10014, USA
Penguin Books Australia Ltd, Ringwood, Victoria, Australia
Penguin Books Canada Ltd, 10 Alcorn Avenue, Toronto, Ontario,
Canada M4V 3B2
Penguin Books India (P) Ltd, 11 Community Centre, Panchsheel Park,
New Delhi – 110 017, India
Penguin Books (NZ) Ltd, Cnr Rosedale and Airborne Roads,
Albany, Auckland, New Zealand
Penguin Books (South Africa) (Pty) Ltd, 5 Watkins Street, Denver Ext 4,
Johannesburg 2094, South Africa
Penguin Books Ltd, Registered Offices: Harmondsworth, Middlesex, England

First published 2001
1 3 5 7 9 10 8 6 4 2

Printed in England by Clays Ltd, St Ives plc

CONTENTS

HOW TO PLAY

⬬ THE RULES

So you've come this far, but are you smart enough to handle Book 2? Weakest Link is the quiz game with a difference – in order to win, the players must act as a team, working together to build chains of correct answers and round by round getting rid of the person who they think is the weakest link. The aim is to reach the 1000 point target, and the fastest way to do this is to answer a chain of nine correct answers in a row. To become the strongest link you'll need to use both your general knowledge and your strategic skills: should you 'bank' the points in the chain or risk losing them all by failing to answer your question correctly? Can you spot who is the weakest link in the team? Will you crumble under the pressure? Remember, you may leave with nothing. Are you too slow to stay? Will it be you taking the 'walk of shame' as you are voted the weakest link?

Once more you can experience the excitement, tension and sometimes the embarrassment of the TV quiz show by playing the game at home, with *The Weakest Link Quiz Book 2*. Here's a reminder of how to play:

⬬ What You Need

Weakest Link can be played by any number of players but ideally there should be four or more, one of whom will be the quiz master (see page 9 for playing with two or three players or on your own).

Each player will need a pencil and a sheet or pad of paper. The quiz master may also want a pencil and paper to keep a tally of the scores. If you want to give each round a time limit, you will need a watch with a second hand or a stopwatch.

⬬ The Rounds

The quiz master takes the book and opens it to the Questions section. At the beginning of the first round the quiz master asks the first question to the player whose initial is the earliest in the alphabet, the second question to the player on his or her left, and so on, asking each player a question in turn. In the following rounds the person to the left of the last player to answer a question in the previous round is the first to be asked.

The length of each round can be determined in a number of ways:

Timing: As in *The Weakest Link* TV programme, each round can have a time limit, starting with 3 minutes for the first round, and cutting off

10 seconds with each further round. Round two would therefore be 2 minutes 50 seconds, round three 2 minutes 40 seconds, round four 2 minutes 30 seconds, and so on. In this case you may use up the questions of more than two pages in each round. In the first round the quiz master will have to keep watch on the time; in later rounds one of the eliminated players could be responsible for timing.

20 Questions: You could limit each round to 20 questions (two pages of the book).

Questions Per Player: Alternatively you could decide to ask each player three, four or five questions in each round. Again, the quiz master might use up the questions on more than two pages and would have to carry the scoring over.

Scoring

The quiz master is responsible for keeping a tally of the team's score for each round, using the points chain on each right-hand page. At the beginning of the round, he or she puts a finger on the bottom link of the chain, the 20. This is the amount that the first question is worth. If the question is answered correctly, the quiz master will move his or her finger up to the next link - 50. If the second question is answered correctly he or she moves it up to the third link - 100, and the team has gained 50 points. Scoring continues in this manner either until the end of the round or when the target is reached.

The aim of the players is to work together as a team to win as many points as possible during the round. To do this they must bank the points before the chain is broken by a wrong answer or before the round comes to an end. They do this by calling 'bank' when it comes to their turn to answer a question, but before the question has been asked. When 'bank' is called it is the amount of points that is below the quiz master's finger that actually goes into the bank. So if his/her finger is on 100 when 'bank' is called, the team has banked 50. The quiz master writes down the points banked either in the spaces provided or on a separate piece of paper. The quiz master then puts his or her finger back on 20 to start a new chain and asks the player who has banked the points his or her question. If the players reach their 1000 point target the round finishes early. They cannot exceed 1000 points per round.

It is up to the skill and judgement of each player whether to bank the points, thereby securing the points but breaking the chain, or to carry on and try to build the chain higher, but risk losing it all if they can't answer correctly. The question is, will you cope? Are you better off watching the show on television rather than actually attempting to play the game?

If the last person to be questioned in the round does not call 'bank' before his or her question, the points on the current chain are lost. The players cannot see the chain, but to help them keep track of how the points are building, the quiz master should shout out 'chain broken' at the beginning of each chain (that is, whenever a question is answered incorrectly, or the points are banked). At the end of each round, only points that have been banked will go through to the next round.

At the end of the first round the quiz master adds up all the points banked. This balance is then brought forward to the next round, and can be written in the space at the top of the next right-hand page to keep a running total of the points for the game.

The Weakest Link

At the end of each round, each player must decide who has been the weakest link, answering the fewest questions correctly or failing to bank points. The players write their selection on their pieces of paper, which they hold up at the same time. The player with the most votes is the weakest link and is sent of with the words 'You are the weakest link...Goodbye!'

In the event of a draw, responsibility for naming the weakest link lies with those who have already been voted off as weakest links. These players should continue to keep track of the game so that they can cast their votes if necessary. And maybe settle some old scores!

Once the weakest link has been decided, the quiz master starts a new round with the remaining players.

The Last Round

In the last round, when there are only two players left, they have the opportunity to increase their points by trebling their total for the round. This is then added to the running total for the previous rounds. It is these points that the players will then play for in the final.

Head to Head

After the last round the two remaining players go head-to-head in a final battle to establish, once and for all, who is the strongest link. The players take it in turns to answer five questions each. The quiz master should mark each question with a tick if it is answered correctly, or a cross if it is answered incorrectly, in the spaces provided. The player who was the strongest link in the previous round (as decided by either the quiz master or the players who are no longer in the game) can decide whether to answer first or second.

The player who answers the most questions correctly is the winner, and the strongest link. If there is a tie after five questions 'sudden death' questions are asked until there is a winner.

Sudden Death

The questions continue in pairs. If player a) gets their question correct then player b) will have to answer their question correctly to win. If player a) gets their question wrong then player b) will have to answer their question correct to win.

Playing with Two or Three Players

You can use *The Weakest Link Quiz Book 2* to test the general knowledge and skill of two or three players. In this case, players should take it in turns to ask a round of questions to one opponent. After each question the player has the chance to bank his or her points or continue and try to build up the chain of points.

After 20 questions, or if you wish to time the rounds three minutes, the round ends and the player's points are counted. That player then becomes the quiz master for the next round. If there are three players, he will question the third player, who will then test the first quiz master in the next round. If there are two players they simply take it in turns to be quiz master. After a set number of rounds, decided before the beginning of the game, the player with the most points is the winner.

Testing Your Own Knowledge

Of course, you can also use *The Weakest Link Quiz Book 2* on your own to test your general knowledge. Try to answer 20 questions, then check to see how many you got right. Cover up the answers until the end of the round! Allocate yourself one point for each question answered correctly and see if you can improve your score with the next round.

Remember...

You have to be ruthless to be rich. Are you up to it? It's time to find out. Let's play the Weakest Link...

1 Complete the title of this Scottish Highland sport: 'Tossing the . . .' what?

2 What *D* are a series of events or images perceived in the mind during sleep?

3 Which children's animated TV series about trains was narrated by Ringo Starr?

4 What was the profession of Florence Nightingale during the Crimean War?

5 A manicure is cosmetic treatment of what part of the body?

6 What *A* is a small unused organ which shares its name with an addition to the end of a book?

7 In food, which *B* is a long French stick of bread with a crispy crust?

8 What type of games are 'cribbage' and 'patience'?

9 In the UK, does the M1 motorway connect London and Lancashire or London and Yorkshire?

10 Which Disney film featured the characters Shere Khan and King Louie?

11 Is the state of California on the east or west coast of the USA?

12 What was the title of Elizabeth Gaskell's last novel, *Wives and Daughters* or *Sons and Daughters*?

13 In the children's nursery rhyme, the black sheep had how many bags of wool?

14 Which animals are famed for their sleepiness and take their name from the Latin for 'sleep'?

15 What *L* is a domesticated pack animal of the camel family, found in the Andes, and valued for its soft woolly fleece?

16 Name the German female tennis player who is the only person to have won all four Grand Slams and Olympic gold in the same year.

17 In fashion, what *S* is a high, narrow shoe heel which originated in Italy during the 1950s?

18 Who played prison warden Paul Edgecomb in the 1999 drama *The Green Mile*?

19 According to custom, are white flowers considered lucky or unlucky?

20 What character did actor Larry Hagman play in the US TV soap *Dallas*?

Previous Total

1,000

800

600

450

300

200

100

50

20

Banked

Total

Answers

1 Caber
2 Dreams
3 *Thomas the Tank Engine*
4 Nurse (accept nursing superintendent/ hospital reformer)
5 The hands (accept fingernails)
6 Appendix
7 Baguette
8 Card games
9 London and Yorkshire
10 *The Jungle Book*
11 West
12 *Wives and Daughters*
13 Three
14 Dormice (accept dormouse)
15 Llama
16 Steffi Graf
17 Stiletto
18 Tom Hanks
19 Unlucky
20 J. R. Ewing (John Ross Ewing)

Round 2

1 In the animal kingdom, what A is another name for a donkey?

2 What does the organisation ASH campaign to prevent?

3 In food, what O is eggs that are whisked and then fried?

4 What C is a root vegetable that was first introduced to Britain in the fifteenth century?

5 In maths, what is the square root of 25?

6 Complete the title of this 1962 film starring Bette Davis: *Whatever Happened to Baby . . .*?

7 Popular in the 1870s, what were penny farthings?

8 In the animal kingdom, the name of which animal means 'river horse'?

9 In which children's TV cartoon did a secret agent mouse, voiced by David Jason, have a sidekick voiced by Terry Scott?

10 Which German city is associated with the legend of the Pied Piper?

11 In food, what is the name of the thin, crisp biscuit that is served with ice-cream?

12 In the human body, which twelve pairs of bones protect the lungs and heart?

13 What was the writer James Herriot's other profession?

14 Which pop superstar dropped his name in favour of a symbol?

15 In food, which Italian phrase meaning 'to the tooth' can be used to describe pasta cooked only until it offers a slight resistance when bitten?

16 In nature, what *F* is the term applied to mushrooms, toadstools and moulds?

17 What is the name of the female character played by Australian Barry Humphries, which he calls a 'housewife superstar'?

18 Which toxic gas, produced in car exhausts, has the chemical formula CO?

19 In cockney rhyming slang, what is known as a 'syrup'?

20 In photography, what *T* is the name given to a three-legged camera stand?

Previous Total

1,000

800

600

450

300

200

100

50

20

Banked

Total

Answers

1 Ass
2 Smoking (accept tobacco)
3 Omelette
4 Carrot
5 Five
6 Jane
7 Bicycles
8 Hippopotamus
9 *Dangermouse*
10 Hameln (or Hamelin)
11 Wafer
12 Ribs (accept ribcage)
13 Veterinary surgeon/ vet
14 Prince
15 *Al dente*
16 Fungi
17 (Dame) Edna Everage
18 Carbon monoxide
19 A wig
20 Tripod

Round 3

1. In 1977, Burt Reynolds starred as a lovable outlaw in the first of a series of films entitled *Smokey and the* . . . what?

2. In maths, what is half of 110?

3. The early life of which Lord Mayor of London is often portrayed in pantomime?

4. What N is the name of the international prizes that were first awarded in 1901?

5. In the animal kingdom, is the polar bear a carnivore or a herbivore?

6. In film, which American actress is famous for her roles in *Sister Act* and *Ghost*?

7. What is the capital city of Germany?

8. What H is the limit to which one can see across the surface of the sea or a level plain?

9. How many feet are there in three yards?

10. Adolf Fick invented which optical aid in 1887?

11. What was the name of the famous rock festival held in New York State in 1969?

12. In the animal kingdom, which runs faster, the emu or the ostrich?

13. Which famous Elizabethan theatre in Southwark was rebuilt and opened in 1996, near its original site?

14. In nature, which C is a case that protects butterflies and moths as they change from larvae into adults?

15 In the 1980 film *The Elephant Man*, which Welsh actor played the part of Dr Frederick Treves?

16 In the animal kingdom, is there such thing as a snapping turtle?

17 In art, in which century was the Cubist movement founded?

18 What *F* is the word used to describe abstinence observed by followers of various religions during Yom Kippur, Ramadan and Lent?

19 Was Johann Strauss's waltz *The Blue Danube* first performed in Vienna or Berlin?

20 *Wish You Were Here* was a 1975 album made by which British rock band?

Previous Total

1,000

800

600

450

300

200

100

50

20

Banked

Total

Answers

1 Bandit	**11** Woodstock
2 55	**12** Ostrich
3 Dick Whittington (Sir Richard Whittington)	**13** Globe Theatre
4 Nobel (Prizes)	**14** Cocoon
5 Carnivore	**15** (Sir) Anthony Hopkins
6 Whoopi Goldberg	**16** Yes
7 Berlin	**17** Twentieth
8 Horizon	**18** Fasting (accept fast)
9 Nine	**19** Vienna
10 Contact lens (accept glass contact lens)	**20** Pink Floyd

Round 4

1 In nature, what O is a type of farming opposed to the use of synthetic fertilisers and pesticides?

2 Which *Batman* star was born Michael Douglas and therefore had to change his name?

3 What type of medieval weapon fires a 'bolt' or 'quarrel'?

4 In medicine, 'peptic', 'duodenal' and 'gastric' are all types of what condition?

5 Which author wrote *Murder at the Vicarage* in 1930?

6 In the animal kingdom, does a tarantula spin a web?

7 Who was Edmund Hillary's guide when he became the first man to reach the summit of Everest in 1953?

8 In which comics did Spiderman and the X-Men first appear, DC comics or Marvel comics?

9 In geology, what E are the 'Palaeozoic', 'Mesozoic' and 'Cenozoic'?

10 Which Clare was first elected Labour MP for Birmingham Ladywood in 1983?

11 In sport, which Scottish city has football teams nicknamed the 'Jam Tarts' and 'Hibs'?

12 Which spiky-haired violinist took Vivaldi's *Four Seasons* to number one in the UK classical album charts in 1989?

13 In human biology, where in the body is the 'aqueous humour'?

14 Singer Mick Hucknall is a member of which pop group?

15 What type of baby clothing was first introduced in 1949 in Britain?

16 How many pence are there in one hundred pounds?

17 Which country derives its name from that of the Aztec war god, Mextili?

18 In sport, did Jonathan Davies play Rugby Union, Rugby League, or both?

19 Which boy's name can be placed before 'knife', 'pot' and 'hammer' to make new words?

20 Which British fashion designer – the daughter of a former Beatle – launched her own fashion label when she graduated from St Martin's in 1995?

Previous Total

1,000

800

600

450

300

200

100

50

20

Banked

Total

Answers

1 Organic (farming)
2 Michael Keaton
3 Crossbow
4 Ulcers
5 Agatha Christie
6 No
7 Sherpa Tenzing Norgay (accept Tenzing Norgay/ Sherpa Tenzing)
8 Marvel
9 Era (do not accept epoch or eon)
10 Clare Short
11 Edinburgh
12 Nigel Kennedy (accept Kennedy)
13 In the eye
14 Simply Red
15 Disposable nappies (accept Paddipads)
16 Ten thousand
17 Mexico
18 Both
19 Jack
20 Stella McCartney

Round 5

1 Norris McWhirter was put 'On The Spot' on what children's show about the *Guinness Book of Records*?

2 What *F* is commonly a unit of water-depth measurement, originally the distance between a man's fingertips with his arms outstretched?

3 Which *G* is the study of family origins?

4 In classical music, which ensemble has more players, a symphony orchestra or a chamber orchestra?

5 Did Givenchy or Dior design costumes for the film *Breakfast at Tiffany's*?

6 Welshman Leighton Rees became which pub sport's first world professional champion in 1978?

7 What *L* is a small European state near Switzerland which did not give women the vote until 1984?

8 Which town in the UK has the larger population, Reading or Swindon?

9 What toy was invented in 1955, the name of which derives from the Danish term meaning 'to play well'?

10 In what year did evacuations of children out of major cities and towns begin in Britain, at the outbreak of hostilities in World War II?

11 If you potted the following snooker balls, how many points would you score: one red, one pink?

12 Which *C* is a musical term meaning 'gradually getting louder'?

13 In Australia, what type of animal is a 'bandicoot', a marsupial or a lizard?

14 The members of which religion are followers of the 'Eightfold Path'?

15 In sport, what is the name of the target in curling, a tee or a bull's-eye?

16 In film, in which decade was the Fellini movie *La Dolce Vita* released?

17 In folklore, how many leaves does a lucky clover have?

18 In medicine, what *T* is a name given to a transfer of tissue or an organ from one human being to another?

19 What *S* is a variety of beer made from heavily roasted malts?

20 Who wrote the classic novel *Far from the Madding Crowd*?

Previous Total

1,000

800

600

450

300

200

100

50

20

Banked

Total

Answers

1 *Record Breakers*	**12** Crescendo
2 Fathom	**13** Marsupial
3 Genealogy	**14** Buddhism
4 Symphony orchestra	**15** Tee
5 Givenchy	**16** 1960s
6 Darts	**17** Four
7 Liechtenstein	**18** Transplant (*do not*
8 Swindon	accept transfusion –
9 Lego	transfer of blood/fluid)
10 1939	**19** Stout
11 7 points (1 + 6)	**20** Thomas Hardy

Round 6

1 Is meiosis a type of cell joining or cell division?

2 What was the name of the American TV science-fiction series of the 1990s in which the character Samuel Beckett would 'jump' into the lives of different people?

3 What is the UK politician Mo Mowlam's full first name?

4 Which Russian leader eliminated all opposition between 1936 and 1938 in the 'Great Purge'?

5 In music, which famous American family pop group achieved hits with 'I Want You Back' and 'ABC'?

6 In which UK country would you find Midlothian Unitary Authority?

7 In politics, who introduced the 'Citizens' Charter': Margaret Thatcher, John Major or Tony Blair?

8 Which Indian city has been nicknamed 'Bollywood'?

9 In literature, Titania is a character from which Shakespeare play?

10 Which year saw the first cricket test match between England and Australia in Melbourne, 1860 or 1877?

11 Which European capital city is known as 'Moskva' in its native language?

12 In medicine, what O is a complementary practice involving treatment of many joint and muscular disorders by manipulation and massage?

13 Did Prokofiev compose the music for the opera The Love for Three Peaches or The Love for Three Oranges?

14 In the Bible, who was the father of Esau and Jacob?

15 In the USA, in which state would you find Chicago and Rockford?

16 Which photographic technique, first demonstrated in 1963, employs lasers to obtain a three-dimensional image?

17 What twenty-four-hour car race was first staged in France in 1923?

18 From which continent are the Masai, Mashona and Matabele tribes?

19 In mythology, what nationality was hero Finn MacCool?

20 In which British university city would you find the Bodleian Library and Christopher Wren's Sheldonian Theatre?

Previous Total

1,000

800

600

450

300

200

100

50

20

Banked

Total

Answers

1 Division
2 *Quantum Leap*
3 Marjorie
4 Stalin (accept Joseph Stalin)
5 The Jackson Five
6 Scotland
7 John Major
8 Bombay
9 *A Midsummer Night's Dream*
10 1877
11 Moscow
12 Osteopathy
13 *Oranges*
14 Isaac
15 Illinois
16 Holography (accept hologram/lensless photography)
17 Le Mans
18 Africa
19 Irish
20 Oxford

Round 7

1 If there are eleven French francs to the pound, how many francs are there in £20?

2 In UK politics, for which party was Tony Banks elected MP for West Ham in 1997?

3 From October to December 2000, the England cricket team toured which country for the first time in thirteen years?

4 In nature, what M is a thin barrier made up of lipid and protein molecules separating the cell contents from its surroundings?

5 What is the English name of the Welsh national anthem?

6 What is the central bank of the United Kingdom?

7 Which children's TV show is set in Pontypandy?

8 The name of which country is derived from that of Italian explorer Amerigo Vespucci?

9 Which pop singer's hundredth single was called 'The Best of Me' and was released in 1989?

10 In literature, Sarah Woodruff is whose woman, according to the title of John Fowles's novel?

11 In the human body, the skin is made up of two layers – the epidermis and what other?

12 In television, who was the first presenter of the children's programme Crackerjack in 1955?

13 In geography, Norfolk Island in the South Pacific is in which country's territory?

14 Who became president of France in 1981?

15 Martin Kemp and Steve Norman from the pop band Spandau Ballet appeared as players in which football comic strip in 1985?

16 Which 1959 musical was Rodgers and Hammerstein's last collaboration?

17 Which TV sports programme, first shown in 1958, has included David Coleman and Frank Bough amongst its presenters?

18 Omar Sharif starred in which 1965 film adaptation of Pasternak's epic novel of the Russian Revolution?

19 From which country does the shiatsu method of massage originate?

20 Associated with the story of Moses, what *B* is the popular alternative name of the plant the 'reed mace'?

Previous Total

1,000

800

600

450

300

200

100

50

20

Banked

Total

Answers

1 220 francs
2 Labour
3 Pakistan
4 Membrane
5 *Land of My Fathers*
6 The Bank of England
7 *Fireman Sam*
8 America
9 (Sir) Cliff Richard
10 *The French Lieutenant's Woman*
11 Dermis
12 Eamonn Andrews
13 Australia
14 François Mitterrand
15 *Roy of the Rovers* (accept Roy Race)
16 *The Sound of Music*
17 *Grandstand*
18 *Doctor Zhivago*
19 Japan
20 Bulrush

Round 8

1 According to the proverb, an army marches on its what?

2 Porkpie, bowler and beanie are all types of what clothing?

3 What *R* is a small carpet?

4 In the 1960s TV sitcom *The Addams Family*, what was the name of the butler?

5 What *F* describes an abnormally high body temperature, often accompanied by shivering and headaches?

6 Which syrupy liquid is made by bees from the nectar of flowers?

7 Flat racing involves what type of four-legged animal?

8 What were the two first names of Bell, the inventor of the telephone?

9 In children's toys, what is the name of the toy figure that springs out of a box when it is opened?

10 What *H* is the horny casing of the toe of some mammals in place of a claw?

11 Did computer floppy disks get their name because they were originally floppy?

12 What is the name of the London street off Whitehall that is home to the prime minister?

13 Does the 1976 film *Bugsy Malone* feature a cast of animals or children?

14 Who invented the saxophone, Adolphe Sax or Herbert Horn?

15 In literature, who is Sue Townsend's most famous schoolboy creation?

16 In pop music, what is the nickname of Melanie Brown from the Spice Girls?

17 Which famous ocean liner, Britain's largest, made its maiden voyage in 1969?

18 In which snooker-related pub game must players avoid knocking over wooden pegs when potting balls?

19 Which TV cartoon cat was frequently chased by Officer Dibble and was loosely based on *Sergeant Bilko*?

20 In the animal kingdom, which C in the ape family is known for its high intelligence?

Previous Total

1,000
800
600
450
300
200
100
50
20

Banked

Total

Answers

1 Stomach
2 Hat(s)
3 Rug (accept runner)
4 Lurch
5 Fever
6 Honey
7 Horse
8 Alexander Graham
9 Jack-in-the-box
10 Hoof
11 Yes
12 Downing Street
13 Children

14 Adolphe Sax
15 Adrian Mole
16 Scary (accept Scary Spice/Mel B/Mel G)
17 QE2 (accept Queen Elizabeth the Second)
18 Bar billiards
19 Top Cat (accept Boss Cat)
20 Chimpanzee (accept chimp)

Round 9

1 In science, what do thermometers and pyrometers measure?

2 Traditionally, from which material is a hula skirt made?

3 In music, is a mandolin a string or wind instrument?

4 Now a BBC sports presenter, which British tennis player won the 1976 French Open women's title?

5 According to superstition, which shoulder should you throw spilt salt over to avoid bad luck?

6 In classical music, does an overture come at the beginning or end of an opera?

7 In the human body, what C is a prolonged, painful contraction of a muscle?

8 The Taj Mahal is usually considered to be the most famous of the ancient buildings of which country?

9 What was the name of the Rat puppet character of the 1980s, who had a sidekick called Kevin the Gerbil?

10 In nature, which M is a type of plant that grows on moist ground and has stems and leaves but no true roots?

11 Which crime novelist also wrote the plays *Black Coffee* and *The Mousetrap*?

12 In October 2000, which British film star and model broke an actors' strike because of a TV commercial she filmed?

13 In the animal kingdom, can a kiwi bird fly?

14 In what part of the UK is Snowdonia, Wales or Scotland?

15 Which fairy-tale play by J. M. Barrie, first performed in 1904, was subtitled The Boy Who Would Not Grow Up?

16 What is the name of Mick Jagger's jewellery designer daughter?

17 What voluntary medical donation service was established in 1921 by four Red Cross members?

18 Which *B* is the second largest city in England?

19 In the animal kingdom, is an oriole a type of bird or insect?

20 In television, what was the name of the Irish priest who shared a house on Craggy Island with Father Dougal and Father Jack?

Previous Total

1,000

800

600

450

300

200

100

50

20

Banked

Total

Answers

1 Temperature (accept heat)
2 Grass (accept dried grass)
3 String
4 Sue Barker
5 Left
6 Beginning
7 Cramp
8 India
9 Roland (Rat)
10 Moss
11 Agatha Christie
12 Elizabeth Hurley
13 No
14 Wales
15 *Peter Pan*
16 Jade Jagger (accept Jade)
17 Blood donation (accept blood donor)
18 Birmingham
19 Bird
20 Father Ted (Father Ted Crilly)

Round 10

1 Val Kilmer played the part of Jim Morrison in which Oliver Stone film about the pop group of the same name?

2 In nature, what *E* is a river mouth widening into the sea, where fresh water mixes with salt water?

3 Which magazine campaigns against homelessness and first hit the streets in 1991?

4 In food, what is the French term on a menu signifying that each item is priced separately?

5 In environmental science, what term is given to the trapping of heat by gases in the earth's atmosphere?

6 In human biology, what *S* is the organ situated on the left-hand side of the body between the diaphragm and stomach?

7 In the animal kingdom, the giant panda is native to which country?

8 In history, what was the assumed name of Malcolm Little, the US Black nationalist leader?

9 In television, on which Gerry Anderson puppet show was bespectacled nine-year-old Joe McClaine the most special agent?

10 Which American singer played the title role in the 1985 film *Desperately Seeking Susan*?

11 In food, pecan and pistachio are varieties of what *N*?

12 In Greek mythology, who was the beautiful youth who was loved by Aphrodite?

13 For what do the initials RSPCA stand?

14 In music, 'Addicted to Love' was a 1986 hit for which Yorkshire-born singer?

15 In science, what *P* is the effect of force on an area?

16 What is the capital city of Russia?

17 Was the year 2000 AD a leap year?

18 What do the initials WC stand for on a lavatory door?

19 Front of . . . what is the term applied to the areas of the theatre which are used by the audience?

20 In the Roman Catholic Church, which is the higher ranking, archbishop or cardinal?

Previous Total

1,000

800

600

450

300

200

100

50

20

Banked

Total

Answers

1 The Doors	**12** Adonis
2 Estuary	**13** Royal Society for the
3 The Big Issue	Prevention of Cruelty
4 A la carte	to Animals
5 Greenhouse effect	**14** Robert Palmer
6 Spleen	**15** Pressure
7 China	**16** Moscow
8 Malcolm X	**17** Yes
9 Joe 90	**18** Water closet
10 Madonna	**19** Front of house
11 Nut(s)	**20** Cardinal

Round 11

1 In which part of the human body would you find the pharynx?

2 What *L* is an engine for hauling railway trains?

3 PC George Dixon was one of Britain's longest-serving TV policemen in which series, from 1955 to 1976?

4 In maths, what is the sum of all the interior angles in any quadrilateral?

5 What *W* is a low wall or barrier built across a river to raise the water level?

6 Which American term for a dinner jacket is derived from the name of a fashionable New York country club?

7 Which London park has an open-air theatre and a zoo?

8 In the lyrics of which Elvis hit did the warden throw a party in the county jail?

9 If a scooter travels at 20 miles per hour, how many miles will it travel in half an hour?

10 In the animal kingdom, gentoo, little blue and emperor are all varieties of which creature?

11 In which year did the first Superman comic strip appear, 1938 or 1945?

12 What is the name of the legendary slave writer to whom authorship of many Greek fables is attributed?

13 In which century did Madrid become the capital of Spain, the seventeenth or nineteenth?

14 Which *I* is the term used to denote the artificial hatching of eggs through mechanical means?

15 In the USA, Indianapolis is the capital of which state?

16 In religion, what is the popular name of the section of the Western Wall in Jerusalem where Jewish pilgrims gather to pray and lament the destruction of the Temple?

17 In television, which broadcaster has a teletext service called Ceefax?

18 Which US state is further south, Kansas or Oklahoma?

19 In science, non-conductive materials such as plastic and rubber are known as what *I*?

20 In the animal kingdom, is the sun bear the smallest or largest of the bear family?

Previous Total

1,000

800

600

450

300

200

100

50

20

Banked

Total

Answers

1 Throat (accept neck)
2 Locomotive (accept loco)
3 *Dixon of Dock Green*
4 360 degrees
5 Weir
6 Tuxedo
7 Regent's Park
8 'Jailhouse Rock'
9 10 miles
10 Penguin
11 1938
12 Aesop
13 Seventeenth
14 Incubate (accept incubation)
15 Indiana
16 Wailing Wall
17 BBC (accept BBC1 or BBC2)
18 Oklahoma
19 Insulators
20 Smallest

Round 12

1 What B is a felt-like, woollen fabric, usually green, used for the tops of snooker or card tables?

2 Who was defeated at the Battle of Flodden in 1513, the Scots or the English?

3 The American Revolution of 1775 to 1783 is also known by what other name?

4 In which decade was the singer and songwriter Michael Jackson born?

5 In food, pippin and discovery are types of which fruit?

6 Which sport featured in the Kevin Costner films *Bull Durham* and *Field of Dreams*?

7 In which hemisphere would you find a boreal forest, northern or southern?

8 In government, for what do the letters CSA stand?

9 What is the occupation of Kieren Fallon and Frankie Dettori?

10 In which country is the winter sports resort of St Moritz?

11 Which 1998 Oscar-winning film has the tag line 'A Comedy About the Greatest Love Story Almost Never Told'?

12 In which country might you visit the Bungle Bungles and Wagga Wagga?

13 Which of the following two men was a famous Scottish writer, Sir Walter Scott or Robert Falcon Scott?

14 In science, is neon a solid, liquid or gas under normal conditions?

15 In nature, what *L* is the name given to any member of the pea and bean family?

16 How much would the phone bill be in pounds and pence if you made eighty local calls at four pence each?

17 Name the 1980s British romantic comedy which starred Paul Nicholas as Vince Pinner and Jan Francis as Penny Warrender.

18 Bauhaus was a school of architecture in which European country?

19 Which of these cities is further from London by plane, Rome or Salzburg?

20 In nature, what *S* is the name for the grasslands of Asia?

Previous Total

( )

(1,000)

(800)

(600)

(450)

(300)

(200)

(100)

(50)

(20)

Banked

( )

( )

( )

( )

( )

Total

( )

Answers

1 Baize
2 Scots
3 American War of Independence
4 1950s
5 Apple
6 Baseball
7 Northern
8 Child Support Agency
9 Jockey
10 Switzerland
11 *Shakespeare in Love*
12 Australia
13 Sir Walter Scott
14 Gas
15 Legume
16 £3.20
17 *Just Good Friends*
18 Germany
19 Rome
20 Steppe(s)

Round 13

1 What is the highest mountain in Northern Ireland, Slieve Donard or Sligo Bridget?

2 In nature, the world's tallest living tree is found in which state in the USA?

3 In which country did the Bay of Pigs invasion take place?

4 Which British-born actress starred as Jessica Fletcher in the 1980s TV series *Murder, She Wrote*?

5 In which country might you visit Edfu and Aswan?

6 In international trade, what Q is a limitation on the quantities exported or imported?

7 In which English shire county would you find the Cotswolds, the Severn Valley and the Forest of Dean?

8 In which 1971 Oscar-winning film did Gene Hackman play Jimmy 'Popeye' Doyle, a cop on the trail of a French drug-trafficker?

9 In music, Father McKenzie features in the lyrics of which Beatles song?

10 Which South-western American state is the only one to have been an independent republic prior to joining the Union?

11 With which sport would you associate Juan Manuel Fangio?

12 In which country is the Vikram Seth novel *A Suitable Boy* set?

13 Which children's TV programme had a character called Bungle?

14 On which side of the road do cars drive in Australia?

15 Which artist's work between 1901 and mid-1904 is known as his 'Blue Period'?

16 Was the philosopher David Hume Scottish, English or Welsh?

17 What 1986 animated film features a Russian mouse separated from his family in their new homeland, America?

18 Which British female comedy duo embarked on their first live national tour in eleven years in November 2000?

19 In classical music, was the composer Béla Bartók born in Hungary or Finland?

20 In food, what *P* is a dessert made of meringue, cream and fresh fruit?

Previous Total
1,000
800
600
450
300
200
100
50
20

Banked

Total

Answers

1 Slieve Donard	**12** India
2 California	**13** *Rainbow*
3 Cuba	**14** Left
4 Angela Lansbury	**15** Pablo Picasso (accept
5 Egypt	Picasso)
6 Quota	**16** Scottish
7 Gloucestershire	**17** *An American Tail*
8 *The French Connection*	**18** Dawn French and
9 'Eleanor Rigby'	Jennifer Saunders
10 Texas	**19** Hungary
11 Motor racing	**20** Pavlova

Round 14

1 In the sitcom, Sharon and Tracey are *Birds* of a what?

2 According to the proverb, every what has a silver lining?

3 In which board game do forty rectangles represent properties, including railways, utilities and a jail?

4 Which fruit is traditionally used to produce cider?

5 In humans, what name is given to the loud noise during sleep caused by vibration of the soft palate?

6 With what sport would you associate Pete Sampras?

7 In fashion, which *M* is a cylindrical accessory for keeping the hands warm?

8 According to superstition, breaking what is said to bring seven years' bad luck?

9 When would you use flies, plugs, spinners and spoons?

10 The Brothers Grimm tale of 'Little Red Cap' became better known as what?

11 What mode of air transport was pioneered in the eighteenth century by the Montgolfier brothers?

12 Which talking scarecrow was the best-known creation of Barbara Euphan Todd?

13 In music, which quiff-haired pop star originally had a hit with 'C'mon Everybody' in the 1950s, Cliff Richard or Eddie Cochrane?

14 Which *F* is a style of dance sometimes performed with castanets?

15 Is a chub an animal or a plant?

16 In food, which term is applied to those who consume no foods of animal origin including dairy products and eggs?

17 In humans, what name is given to the effect of a sudden switch of time zones in air travel?

18 Which cartoon dog is friends with Fred, Daphne, Velma and Shaggy and has a nephew called Scrappy?

19 In theatre, what S is the term used for the scenery and surroundings on the stage?

20 In the nineteenth century, where did women wear a bustle, around the neck or waist?

Answers

1 Feather
2 Cloud
3 Monopoly
4 Apples
5 Snoring
6 Tennis (accept lawn tennis)
7 Muff
8 A mirror (accept looking glass)
9 Angling (accept fishing)
10 'Little Red Riding Hood'
11 Hot air ballooning (accept air ballooning/ ballooning)
12 Worzel Gummidge
13 Eddie Cochrane
14 Flamenco
15 Animal (fish)
16 Vegans (do not accept vegetarians)
17 Jet lag (accept desynchronosis)
18 Scooby-Doo
19 Set
20 Waist

Previous Total

1,000
800
600
450
300
200
100
50
20

Banked

Total

Round 15

1 Which actor says the line 'I'll be back' in the 1984 film *The Terminator*?

2 In London, is Waterloo Station north or south of the river?

3 From which musical comes the lyric 'Everything free in America, For a small fee in America'?

4 In the animal kingdom, what type of creature is a kite?

5 Which feline cartoon character appeared on the titles of the Inspector Clouseau films?

6 Which British crime novelist wrote *Murder at the Vicarage* and *Murder in Mesopotamia*?

7 Macadamia and almond are types of what?

8 On a supermarket shelf there are twelve boxes of eggs each containing a dozen eggs. How many eggs are on the shelf?

9 Which member of the comedy duo Fry and Laurie rewrote the West End and Broadway musical *Me and My Girl*?

10 In fashion, the floppy, rubber-soled sandals, often worn on the beach, are known as 'flip' what?

11 What *P* is a large farm or estate handling the commercial production of a crop?

12 In the UK, which town is known as the 'Gateway to the Lakes' and is famous for its mint cake?

13 Which fruit is generally bigger, a kumquat or a clementine?

14 In pop music, what was the surname of Janis, the rock singer born in Texas in 1943?

15 In the animal kingdom, what C is a type of Australian parrot, usually with grey or yellow plumage, yellow cheeks and a crest?

16 A Black Russian cocktail is made with one part coffee liqueur and two parts of what spirit?

17 Which TV presenter set up the charity Childline in 1986?

18 In science, charcoal is a form of what element?

19 In astrology, the star sign Pisces is represented by what animal?

20 Which long-running TV programme about antiques has been presented by Hugh Scully and Michael Aspel?

Previous Total
1,000
800
600
450
300
200
100
50
20
Banked
Total

Answers

1 Arnold Schwarzenegger	**11** Plantation
2 South	**12** Kendal
3 *West Side Story*	**13** Clementine
4 Bird	**14** Joplin
5 The Pink Panther	**15** Cockatoo (accept cockatiel)
6 Agatha Christie	**16** Vodka
7 Nuts (accept trees)	**17** Esther Rantzen
8 144	**18** Carbon
9 Stephen Fry	**19** Fish
10 Flops (accept flip-flops)	**20** *Antiques Roadshow*

Round 16

1 In language, for what does the abbreviation VIP stand?

2 The name of which district within the city of Los Angeles is synonymous with the American motion-picture industry?

3 In art, what *E* is a method of engraving in which the design is bitten into the plate with acid?

4 By what first name was the actress Dame Edith Margaret Emily Ashcroft usually known?

5 Which American rock group had hits in the 1970s including 'Lyin' Eyes' and 'Hotel California'?

6 In geography, what *I* is the supply of water to the land by means of channels, streams and sprinklers?

7 Which sort of cards include The Hermit and The Hanged Man?

8 Morecambe and Wise ended their TV shows with the song 'Bring Me . . .' what?

9 Which cricketer, nicknamed 'Beefy', captained England in 1980 and 1981?

10 Published in book form in 1883, what is the title of Robert Louis Stevenson's children's story about pirates?

11 In nature, which part of the flower structure attracts insects and guides them towards the stigma and anther?

12 When a muscle contracts does it get longer or shorter?

13 In money, what is the highest-value note in circulation in Germany, the 100 or 1000 Deutschmark note?

14 Is the folk-song 'Greensleeves' mentioned in *Macbeth* or *The Merry Wives of Windsor*?

15 What are non-working male bees called?

16 What *P* is the natural outer covering that houses seeds like beans, lentils and peas?

17 In history, which Walter was an adventurer and writer who was prominent at the court of Elizabeth I?

18 In which series of children's books by Enid Blyton would you find George and Timmy?

19 On television, what was the name of the 1970s comedy trio that consisted of Tim Brooke-Taylor, Graeme Garden and Bill Oddie?

20 In the animal kingdom, Belgian, Clydesdale and percheron are all breeds of which mammal?

Previous Total

1,000
800
600
450
300
200
100
50
20

Banked

Total

Answers

1 Very Important Person
2 Hollywood
3 Etching (do not accept engraving)
4 Peggy
5 The Eagles
6 Irrigation
7 Tarot cards
8 '(Bring Me) Sunshine'
9 Ian Botham
10 *Treasure Island*
11 Petals (accept corolla/perianth)
12 Shorter
13 1000 Deutschmark note
14 *The Merry Wives of Windsor*
15 Drone(s)
16 Pod
17 (Sir) Walter Raleigh
18 *The Famous Five*
19 *The Goodies*
20 Horse

Round 17

1 What *D* describes the removal of all water from a substance?

2 Which Californian pop band first recorded the song 'Barbara Ann' in 1966?

3 Which sport would you be watching if you saw the Baltimore Ravens play the Carolina Panthers?

4 What *D* is the name given to ancient Celtic priests and scholars?

5 The kangaroo and which bird are on the Australian coat of arms?

6 In geography, is Mount Fuji in Japan or Taiwan?

7 In physics, what *Q* is the modern theory of subatomic particles?

8 In 1981, François Mitterrand became president of which country?

9 The Royal Albert Hall in London was completed in which century, the eighteenth or nineteenth?

10 With which sport would you associate Dennis Wise?

11 In medicine, which part of the body is a gastroscope used to examine?

12 In the animal kingdom, frogs and which other amphibians are known as Anurans?

13 24 February 2000 was the third anniversary of the announcement of the birth of which special sheep?

14 In botany, bladderwrack, dulse and kelp are all types of what plant?

15 In which well-known musical would you hear the songs 'I Could Have Danced All Night' and 'On the Street Where You Live'?

16 In which 1998 movie did footballer Vinny Jones make his film debut?

17 In geography, is Vilnius the capital of Lithuania or Macedonia?

18 Which London art gallery houses *The Haywain* by Constable?

19 On the world wide web, which country does '.jp' represent?

20 Which American model starred in the British film *Four Weddings and a Funeral*?

Previous Total

1,000

800

600

450

300

200

100

50

20

Banked

Total

Answers

1 Dehydration (accept desiccation)
2 The Beach Boys
3 American football
4 Druids
5 Emu
6 Japan
7 Quantum theory (accept quantum field theory)
8 France
9 Nineteenth (1871)
10 Football
11 Stomach
12 Toads
13 Dolly
14 Seaweed (accept algae)
15 *My Fair Lady*
16 *Lock, Stock and Two Smoking Barrels*
17 Lithuania
18 The National Gallery
19 Japan
20 Andie MacDowell (accept Rosalie Anderson MacDowell)

Round 18

1 In science, casein is the main protein in which food source, milk or bread?

2 The Austrian capital Vienna is situated on which river?

3 What type of fabric fastening, invented in 1957, uses tiny hooks sticking to tiny loops?

4 Which television personality has made more appearances on the Royal Variety Show, Max Bygraves or Harry Enfield?

5 Did Hawaii or Florida have its own monarch until 1893?

6 In language, for what do the initials RP stand in Britain when meaning the usual speech of educated people?

7 In the UK, Lime Street and James Street are railway stations situated in which northern city?

8 In UK politics, which ex-Northern Ireland Minister was appointed as Cabinet Office Minister in 1999?

9 In America, what D is compulsory military service or conscription?

10 In biology, demography is the study of what?

11 In pop music, which American singer's 1986 autobiography was subtitled 'The Godfather of Soul'?

12 With which city in India was Mother Teresa most closely associated?

13 In which British group of islands would you find Tresco and Bryher?

14 In politics, what do the letters EMU stand for?

15 In literature, who is the narrator of the Charles Dickens novel *David Copperfield*?

16 Who became the first non-Italian pope for 455 years when he was elected in 1978?

17 With which other leader did Stalin sign the Nazi–Soviet Pact in 1939?

18 Followers of which religion fast during the month of Ramadan?

19 In the human body, which *I* is the part of the small intestine where nutrients are absorbed?

20 What is the name given to the popular children's toy, devised by Richard James in the 1940s, made up of several feet of flat wire coiled into circles?

Previous Total

1,000

800

600

450

300

200

100

50

20

Banked

Total

Answers

1 Milk
2 Danube
3 Velcro
4 Max Bygraves
5 Hawaii
6 Received Pronunciation
7 Liverpool
8 Mo Mowlam (accept Marjorie Mowlam)
9 Draft
10 Human populations (accept population/people)
11 James Brown
12 Calcutta
13 Scilly Isles
14 European Monetary Union
15 David (Copperfield)
16 Pope John Paul II (accept Karol Joseph Wojityla; *do not* accept Pope John Paul)
17 Hitler
18 Islam (accept Muslim/Mohammedism)
19 Ileum
20 Slinky

Round 19

1 Which town is further north, Berwick upon Tweed in England or Dumfries in Scotland?

2 Who was the US president during the Bay of Pigs invasion of Cuba?

3 In which country are the cities Trondheim and Oslo?

4 In the UK, Chelmsford is the seat of local government in which county?

5 Is Artemis a figure in Greek or Roman mythology?

6 In literature, what *S* is the surname of the French philosopher Jean-Paul, author of *Nausea* in 1938?

7 In classical music, are wind players or string players concerned with their embouchure?

8 Which essentially Jamaican religion, associated with Marcus Garvey, was named after Ethiopia's crown prince?

9 In literature, which fictional Don attacked a windmill, believing it to be a giant?

10 In geography, eustasy refers to a worldwide change in the level of what?

11 In *King Lear*, what relation is Cordelia to Lear?

12 After *Butch Cassidy and the Sundance Kid*, Paul Newman and Robert Redford starred together in which film about a couple of con men?

13 In science, what is the name given to electric power generated by moving water?

14 Where in Europe was the monarchy restored in 1975 after a 44-year lapse?

15 In biology, are erythrocytes red or white blood cells?

16 Which twentieth-century British prime minister said: 'Economics are the method; the object is to change the soul'?

17 Which 1970s science-fiction TV series, based on Martin Caidin's novel *Cyborg*, starred Lee Majors as Colonel Steve Austin?

18 In which Asian country was satin first made?

19 In the story of David and Goliath, what was David before he killed Goliath, a shepherd or a fisherman?

20 In human biology, where on an infant is the fontanelle?

Previous Total

1,000

800

600

450

300

200

100

50

20

Banked

Total

Answers

1 Berwick upon Tweed
2 John F. Kennedy (accept Kennedy/ JFK/John Fitzgerald Kennedy)
3 Norway
4 Essex
5 Greek
6 Sartre
7 Wind players
8 Rastafarian (accept Rastafarianism)
9 Don Quixote
10 The sea
11 Daughter
12 *The Sting* (1973)
13 Hydroelectric power
14 Spain
15 Red blood cells
16 Margaret Thatcher
17 *The Six Million Dollar Man*
18 China
19 Shepherd
20 Head (accept scalp/ skull)

Round 20

1 The hippie movement of the 1960s was commonly referred to as 'Flower' what?

2 According to the proverb, the what justifies the means?

3 In the TV series *The Muppet Show*, what instrument did Animal usually play?

4 In food, what *P* is a thick dish made of cereal or grain cooked in water or milk?

5 Complete the title of this 1969 hit single by soul singer Marvin Gaye: 'I Heard It Through the . . .' what?

6 What is the name of the folk dance originally thought to have been performed by Scottish men after battles to celebrate victory?

7 What type of creature is a kingfisher?

8 Which dancing partner of Ginger Rogers was born in Omaha, Nebraska in 1899?

9 What *B* is the alphabet for the blind represented by raised dots?

10 In which country of the UK is St David's, the smallest cathedral city in Britain?

11 In pop music, which Irish singer jointly founded and fronted the rock group The Boomtown Rats?

12 In a book by Richard Adams, the characters Speedwell, Toadflax and Bigwig are what kind of animal?

13 In medieval legend, the chalice used by Christ at the Last Supper was known as the Holy what?

14 In film, what is the name given to the pair of hinged boards smacked together during filming to synchronise sound and picture?

15 Is the cobra snake poisonous?

16 In children's cinema, complete the title of this Nick Park and Peter Lord animation from the year 2000: *Chicken* . . . what?

17 Which shoe shares its name with an animal similar to a donkey?

18 In cockney rhyming slang, if someone asked you to pass the 'Army and Navy' at the dinner table, what would they want?

19 What was the title of the 1995 film about a talking pig who herds sheep?

20 What game, featuring black and white pieces, has been known as the royal game because of its popularity among the nobility?

Previous Total
1,000
800
600
450
300
200
100
50
20
Banked
Total

Answers

1 Power	**11** Bob Geldof (Robert Frederick Zenon Geldof)
2 End	
3 Drums (accept drum kit, etc.)	**12** Rabbit
4 Porridge	**13** Grail
5 Grapevine	**14** Clapperboard
6 Highland Fling	**15** Yes
7 Bird	**16** *Run*
8 Fred Astaire (Frederick Austerlitz)	**17** Mule
	18 Gravy
9 Braille	**19** *Babe*
10 Wales	**20** Chess

Round 21

1 In music, what *T* is the word used to describe the speed at which a piece is played?

2 In television, did Joan Collins play Alexis Carrington in *Dynasty* or *Dallas*?

3 Complete the title of this novel by E. Nesbit published in 1906: *The Railway* what?

4 Which female singer had the Supremes as her backing group?

5 In the Bible, who picked fruit from the Tree of the Knowledge of Good and Evil?

6 In nature, are there species of freshwater dolphin?

7 If there are six glasses of wine in one bottle, how many glasses are there in 12 bottles of wine?

8 In history, was Edward III the son or grandson of Edward II?

9 Dizzy Gillespie and Charlie Parker are most commonly associated with which kind of music?

10 Complete the title of the following traditional children's party game, Pin the Tail on the – what?

11 In the animal kingdom, is the prairie dog a rodent or a dog?

12 In the UK, we get water from a tap. What do they call a tap in the US?

13 What name is given to a ceremonial circuit of a sports arena or pitch by the winner?

14 In nature, do plants produce hormones?

15 In food, the potato contains which *S* used in the production of adhesives?

16 Which pop star is older, Tina Turner or Mick Jagger?

17 As well as being a part of the human body, which word describes the calm area at the centre of a hurricane?

18 Is a cockchafer a kind of beetle, wasp or spider?

19 In classical music, what *E* is a French word normally used to refer to a small group of players or singers?

20 The 1999 Formula One world championship was won by Mika who?

Previous Total

1,000

800

600

450

300

200

100

50

20

Banked

Total

Answers

1 Tempo	**11** Rodent
2 Dynasty	**12** Faucet
3 Children	**13** Lap of honour
4 Diana Ross	**14** Yes
5 Eve	**15** Starch
6 Yes	**16** Tina Turner
7 72	**17** Eye
8 Son	**18** Beetle
9 Jazz	**19** Ensemble
10 Donkey	**20** (Mika) Hakkinen

Round 22

1 For which film sequel in 1999 did Tom Hanks provide the voice of the character Woody?

2 In biology, what *B* is fluid produced in the liver and passed through ducts to the small intestine?

3 In the animal kingdom, how many legs does a decapod have?

4 In sport, is kung fu a Chinese or Japanese martial art?

5 Complete the title of this early Shakespeare play: *Love's Labour's* . . . what?

6 In nature, are birds cold-blooded or warm-blooded?

7 In the 1967 film *The Graduate*, what was the surname of the character played by Anne Bancroft, who seduced the young Dustin Hoffman?

8 In human biology, which organ consists of the dermis and epidermis?

9 In history, which Roman emperor led the invasion of Britain in AD 43, Claudius or Augustus?

10 In physics, what C is a substance that permits the free passage of electricity or heat?

11 In which fictional small American town is the 1987 film about three witches set?

12 In which sport is Laura Davies one of the leading female competitors?

13 Which historical English town is home to Jesus Green and Midsummer Common: Oxford or Cambridge?

14 Whose 1979 *Off the Wall* album became the first to contain four US top ten hits?

15 What C is the geological term for a steep-sided gorge cut by a river?

16 Chelsea is the name of which former American president's daughter?

17 27 February 2000 marked the hundredth anniversary of which UK political party?

18 In film, name the actress in *Charlie's Angels* who also starred in *There's Something About Mary*.

19 In politics, in which year did Labour introduce tuition fees in higher education, 1996 or 1998?

20 In the human body, what name is given to the hinge joint between the upper arm and the forearm?

Previous Total

( )

1,000

800

600

450

300

200

100

50

20

Banked

Total

Answers

1 *Toy Story 2* (accept *Toy Story*)
2 Bile
3 Ten
4 Chinese
5 *Lost*
6 Warm-blooded
7 Robinson
8 Skin
9 Claudius
10 Conductor
11 Eastwick (*The Witches of Eastwick*)
12 Golf
13 Cambridge
14 Michael Jackson
15 Canyon (*do not accept chasm*)
16 Bill Clinton
17 Labour
18 Cameron Diaz
19 1998
20 Elbow

Round 23

1 In food, what *B* is the term given to the method of plunging food into boiling water briefly, then into cold water to stop the cooking process?

2 Are the islands of Iona and Staffa situated off Scotland, Ireland or Wales?

3 Name Ridley Scott's 1979 science-fiction film which had the tag line 'In space, no one can hear you scream'.

4 In food, what *P* is French for a young small chicken?

5 In sport, how many consecutive Olympic gold medals has the rower Steve Redgrave won?

6 In Australia, what is the state capital of Victoria?

7 Which star of the films *Boogie Nights* and *Three Kings* first came to fame as an underwear model, Mark Wahlberg or Burt Reynolds?

8 In astronomy, what *C* is the name given to the shape of the moon when it appears less than half illuminated?

9 In basketball, how high above the ground is the hoop: ten feet or twelve feet?

10 In marine biology, by what name is a sea star more commonly known?

11 In history, was Edward the Confessor king of England before or after the Norman Conquest?

12 In pop music, which late British punk rock artist and member of The Sex Pistols was born John Ritchie?

13 In the human body, what *D* is the name given to the teeth also known as milk teeth?

14 In the British police force, for what do the letters CID stand?

15 Which *B* is a UK city that appears in the song title of a Boney M hit?

16 Which is larger, four fifths or seven twelfths?

17 From what type of stone is the Great Sphinx in Egypt carved, limestone or granite?

18 In the USA, which *C* were the original Native Americans of North Carolina?

19 In 1967, which bearded Latin American guerrilla leader became a cult hero after he was shot dead in Bolivia?

20 In classical music, was Maria Callas famous as a singer or a violinist?

Previous Total

1,000

800

600

450

300

200

100

50

20

Banked

Total

Answers

1 Blanching	**12** Sid Vicious
2 Scotland	**13** Deciduous
3 *Alien*	**14** Criminal Investigation
4 Poussin (accept *poulet*)	Department
5 Five	**15** Belfast
6 Melbourne	**16** Four fifths
7 Mark Wahlberg	**17** Limestone
8 Crescent	**18** Cherokee
9 Ten feet	**19** Che Guevara (accept
10 Starfish	Ernesto Guevara)
11 Before	**20** Singer

Round 24

1 In science, what C is the study of the universe as a whole, including its distant past and its future?

2 Which Radio 1 DJ of the 1970s was referred to as 'Diddy'?

3 In which country would you find the industrial port of Le Havre?

4 In art, what G is the practice of applying a layer of gold leaf to the surface of an object and then burnishing it?

5 What name is the process by which a dissolved substance is made less concentrated by the addition of water?

6 Shakespeare lived and worked during which English queen's reign?

7 Does a calorimeter measure heat or fat content?

8 In finance, of which country is the Bundesbank the central bank?

9 In the UK, what term describes the time when clocks are kept one hour ahead of Greenwich Mean Time?

10 Is cobalt a metallic or non-metallic substance?

11 In the year 2000, a stolen Enigma code-breaking machine was returned to which TV presenter?

12 Is the Spanish resort of Tossa de Mar on the Costa Brava or Costa Dorada?

13 According to economic theory, what I is caused by an increase in demand over supply?

14 Was Ariadne a figure in Greek or Roman mythology?

15 Which famous conductor was referred to as 'Andrew Preview' by Eric Morecambe?

16 Which *Monty Python* film features the 'Knights who say "Ni"'?

17 In science, which term applies to the measurement of the electric push of a current?

18 In human biology, what term is given to a pregnancy occurring outside the womb?

19 In terms of population, what Latin American city is the largest in the world?

20 In children's literature, Alice Liddell was the inspiration for which book's heroine?

Previous Total

1,000
800
600
450
300
200
100
50
20

Banked

Total

Answers

1 Cosmology
2 David Hamilton
3 France
4 Gilding
5 Dilution
6 Elizabeth I
7 Heat
8 Germany
9 British Summer Time
10 Metallic
11 Jeremy Paxman
12 Costa Brava
13 Inflation
14 Greek
15 Andre Previn
16 *Monty Python and the Holy Grail* (accept *Holy Grail*)
17 Volt
18 Ectopic pregnancy (accept extrauterine pregnancy)
19 Mexico City
20 *Alice in Wonderland* (accept *Alice Through the Looking Glass*)

Round 25

1 For what does the acronym OPEC stand?

2 In which year of the 1990s was General Pinochet arrested in London on behalf of a Spanish judge?

3 By what name is the Jewish Feast of Dedication known?

4 Which actress, born Betty Joan Perske, began her career as a *Harper's Bazaar* model and took her first leading film role opposite Humphrey Bogart in 1944?

5 In science, what *P* is an alloy of lead and tin?

6 Which plant has leaves that are used in salads, and roots that can be used as a coffee substitute?

7 In film, Peter Fonda and Dennis Hopper starred in which 1969 film about two motorcycling rebels?

8 In a shop, if you were to buy four books at £6.99 each, what would the total cost be?

9 The US TV sitcom *Joanie Loves Chachi* was a spin-off from which long-running show?

10 Which of the Channel Islands has the largest population?

11 Which London art gallery has a purpose-built extension to house its Turner collection?

12 The name of which Caribbean island means 'rich port' in Spanish?

13 In sport, which boxer was known as 'The Brown Bomber' and was heavyweight champion from 1937 to 1949?

14 Which king of England was known as 'Longshanks', Edward I or Richard III?

15 In geometry, what C describes two circles which share the same centre?

16 Who played Dr Latimer in the TV comedy series *Don't Wait Up* and Ralph Gorse in the 1987 drama series *The Charmer*?

17 Which French naval officer and underwater explorer co-invented the aqualung?

18 The American diplomat Henry Kissinger received what prestigious award in 1973?

19 On 14 May 1973, which American space station became the heaviest object ever put into space?

20 Which actor played Flash Harry in the St Trinian's films?

Previous Total

1,000

800

600

450

300

200

100

50

20

Banked

Total

Answers

1 The Organization of Petroleum Exporting Countries
2 1998
3 Hanukkah
4 Lauren Bacall
5 Pewter
6 Chicory
7 *Easy Rider*
8 £27.96
9 *Happy Days*
10 Jersey
11 Tate Britain (accept Tate Gallery)
12 Puerto Rico
13 Joe Louis (accept Joseph Lewis Barrow)
14 Edward I
15 Concentric
16 Nigel Havers
17 Jacques Cousteau
18 Nobel Peace Prize
19 Skylab
20 George Cole

Round 26

1 In Greek legend, what hollow wooden animal was used to smuggle troops into Troy?

2 What *B* is the term for a two-piece bathing suit?

3 In the children's TV animation, what is the name of the postman who owns Jess, a black and white cat?

4 In the animal kingdom, the jellyfish that has long tentacles, armed with powerful stinging cells, is called a Portuguese man-of- what?

5 How many wheels does a unicycle have?

6 Stump-rooted, intermediate and long-rooted are types of which orange-coloured vegetable?

7 Which actor played the part of Dr Hannibal Lecter in the 1991 film *The Silence of the Lambs*?

8 In which board game would you find 'Community Chest' and 'Chance' cards?

9 Which *L* is an Italian dish made from layers of pasta, minced meat and cheese sauce?

10 What colour are the flowers of the buttercup?

11 Complete this proverb: 'Jack of all trades, master of . . .' what?

12 The song 'Unchained Melody' by the Righteous Brothers was played during the pottery-making scene in which 1990 film, starring Demi Moore and Patrick Swayze?

13 In nature, the marsh tit and the garden warbler are both types of which creature?

14 In nature, what *H* is dried, powdered leaves of the Egyptian privet, used to dye hair and skin?

15 Traditionally, a march by Mendelssohn is often played at the end of which church ceremony?

16 In the animal kingdom, what name is given to the male mallard duck?

17 In what part of the body would you find your tricep muscles?

18 Is East Midlands Airport closer to Birmingham, Coventry or Leicester?

19 At the London Palladium, which Australian actor played Joseph in the 1991 version of the musical *Joseph and the Amazing Technicolor Dreamcoat*?

20 In food, which fruit is dried to make a prune?

Previous Total

1,000
800
600
450
300
200
100
50
20

Banked

Total

Answers

1 Horse (Trojan Horse)
2 Bikini
3 Pat
4 (Portuguese man-of-) war
5 One
6 Carrot
7 (Sir) Anthony Hopkins
8 Monopoly
9 Lasagne
10 Yellow
11 None
12 *Ghost*
13 Bird
14 Henna
15 Wedding (accept marriage/wedding service, etc.)
16 Drake
17 Arms (accept top of arms)
18 Leicester
19 Jason Donovan
20 Plum

Round 27

1 In the military, what *A* is the protective covering often worn during fighting?

2 Which famous ballet features the dance of the Sugar Plum Fairy?

3 In professional tennis, does Pete Sampras play left- or right-handed?

4 If you buy five cans of dog food and twice as many cans of cat food, how many cans have you bought?

5 Which pastime involves jumping from bridges or other elevated structures attached to a rubber rope?

6 In measurement, is a US gallon larger or smaller than an imperial gallon?

7 Which singing diva had a UK number one hit in the 1960s called 'Respect'?

8 In modern history, the July Conspiracy of 1944 involved a plot to assassinate which European leader?

9 In science, what *B* is a concentrated solution of salt in water?

10 In which 1982 comedy did Dustin Hoffman play the role of Dorothy Michaels?

11 In which country would you be if you crossed the Tropic of Capricorn on the Stuart Highway, just north of Alice Springs?

12 In athletics, what name is given to the sport of throwing a metal ball weighing between eight and sixteen pounds?

13 In the human body, which A is a hormone secreted by the adrenal gland in times of stress or in response to a fright or shock?

14 In the 1939 film *The Wizard of Oz*, what did the Lion ask the Wizard to give him?

15 What is the name given to the X-shaped stitching which is popular in embroidery?

16 Sumo is the national sport of which country?

17 Name the father of Madonna's second child, Rocco.

18 In America, for what would you use a skillet: cooking or gardening?

19 Which 1977 Steven Spielberg science-fiction film has the tag line 'We Are Not Alone'?

20 In fashion, what is polyvinyl chloride more commonly known as?

Previous Total
1,000
800
600
450
300
200
100
50
20
Banked
Total

Answers

1 Armour
2 *The Nutcracker*
3 Right (-handed)
4 Fifteen
5 Bungee jumping
6 Smaller
7 Aretha Franklin
8 (Adolf) Hitler
9 Brine
10 *Tootsie*
11 Australia
12 Shot put (accept putting the shot)

13 Adrenalin
14 Courage
15 Cross stitch
16 Japan
17 Guy Ritchie
18 Cooking
19 *Close Encounters of the Third Kind* (accept *Close Encounters*)
20 PVC

Round 28

1 In language, which word refers to an irrational fear of an object or situation?

2 What, in the human body, can be ball-and-socket or hinge?

3 Which female singer had a hit with the song 'Babooshka' in 1980?

4 Which Australian soap appeared on British TV first, *Neighbours* or *Home and Away*?

5 If something is translucent, can you see light through it?

6 In which sport is the speed of the ball denoted by the colour of the dot on it?

7 What S is a mark impressed into wax to authenticate letters and documents?

8 Do any humans live in the Sahara desert?

9 Edward Heath was leader of which political party?

10 In children's television, what was the name of the hamster who assisted Dangermouse?

11 In maths, if the length of a rectangle is 15 centimetres and the width is 5 centimetres, what is the perimeter?

12 Is a sturgeon a land or sea creature?

13 In tennis, what L is a high shot intended to land behind an opponent who has approached the net?

14 Complete the title of this play by J. M. Synge: *The Playboy of the Western* what?

15 The first British car registration, A-1, was issued in which century, the nineteenth or twentieth?

16 In British cinema, for what do the initials NFT stand?

17 What *M* is a mixture of lime, cement, sand and water, used for binding bricks and stone when building?

18 In art, what was the nationality of painter Paul Cézanne?

19 In television, Ainsley Harriott took over from Fern Britton as the presenter of which TV cookery show?

20 In the animal kingdom, do the eyes of lions have round or slit pupils?

Previous Total

1,000

800

600

450

300

200

100

50

20

Banked

Total

Answers

1 Phobia
2 Joints
3 Kate Bush
4 *Neighbours* (1986)
5 Yes
6 Squash
7 Seal (accept silluiography; *do not accept signature*)
8 Yes (about 200,000)
9 Conservative Party
10 Penfold (Ernest Penfold)
11 40 centimetres
12 Sea (creature)
13 Lob
14 *World*
15 Twentieth (1903)
16 National Film Theatre
17 Mortar
18 French
19 *Ready, Steady, Cook* (accept *Celebrity Ready, Steady, Cook*)
20 Round

Round 29

1 In which year did Spice Girl Victoria Beckham give birth to her first-born son, Brooklyn?

2 In children's literature, the first book of which Enid Blyton series was published in 1942?

3 General Custer's defeat by the Sioux Indians at Little Bighorn is commonly known as 'Custer's Last . . .' what?

4 In politics, for which London constituency was Glenda Jackson elected MP in 1992: Hampstead and Highgate, or Finchley?

5 In biology, which colour blood cells are correctly known as leucocytes?

6 The American film actress Lauren Bacall married which famous actor in 1945?

7 Zen and Theravada are schools of which religion?

8 Which Essex seaside resort has the world's longest pleasure pier?

9 In television, which British comedian and actor played the character of Rick in *The Young Ones*?

10 In engineering, jib, overhead travelling and tower are all types of what?

11 What G is an association of people of the same trade formed to promote and protect their common interests?

12 Is the state of New Jersey in the east or west of the US?

13 Which theatre in London, on the Waterloo Road, is famous for its Shakespeare productions?

14 Which American Motown artist had a UK hit in 1969 with 'Too Busy Thinking About My Baby'?

15 In science, is argon a gas or a solid at room temperature?

16 Donald Sutherland played the character Hawkeye in which 1970 film?

17 Which word describes a machine designed to work in place of a human and was derived from the Czech for 'forced labour'?

18 In the animal kingdom, is the rhinoceros native to Africa, Asia, or both?

19 In geography, what S is the largest island in the Mediterranean Sea?

20 In literature, which author wrote the children's book *George's Marvellous Medicine*?

Previous Total

1,000
800
600
450
300
200
100
50
20

Banked

Total

Answers

1 1999	**11** Guild
2 Famous Five	**12** East
3 (Custer's Last) Stand	**13** Old Vic (Theatre)
4 Hampstead and Highgate	**14** Marvin Gaye (Marvin Pentz Gay Junior)
5 White (blood cells)	**15** Gas
6 Humphrey Bogart	**16** M*A*S*H
7 Buddhism (accept Buddhist)	**17** Robot
8 Southend-on-Sea (accept Southend)	**18** Both
9 Rik Mayall	**19** Sicily
10 Crane	**20** Roald Dahl

Round 30 ✓

1 In Roman mythology, Flora was the goddess of springtime and what else?

2 In history, was the Battle of Bosworth the first or last battle in the Wars of the Roses?

3 In which country was actor Russell Crowe born?

4 What *H* is the surname of David, one of the leaders of the British Pop Art movement in the 1960s?

5 In food, which contains more vitamin C, lemon juice or lime juice?

6 In UK politics, of which party did Enoch Powell contest the leadership in 1965?

7 One of which sport's world championships is held at the Lakeside Country Club, Frimley Green?

8 A boreal forest is mainly composed of what kind of trees, coniferous or deciduous?

9 Contract and auction are two versions of which card game?

10 Which Australian city is the capital of Queensland?

11 What is the name of the piece of metal that hangs inside a bell?

12 In science, is water a compound or an element?

13 Before 1930, in which country would you have found the city of Constantinople?

14 Rosh Hashanah is the observance of New Year in which religion?

15 In which city in Texas is NASA's Space Center located?

16 Which comedienne, born in Slough, appeared in the TV series *Three of a Kind* before making her name with her own show in America?

17 In transport, do cars have two-stroke or four-stroke engines?

18 Which pop band made history by occupying all of the top five places in the US charts in April 1964?

19 What *L* is the capital city of Peru?

20 In money, is the bolivar the unit of currency in Brazil or Venezuela?

Previous Total

1,000

800

600

450

300

200

100

50

20

Banked

Total

Answers

1 Flowers (accept flowering of plants)
2 Last
3 New Zealand
4 Hockney
5 Lemon juice
6 Conservative (accept Tory)
7 Darts
8 Coniferous
9 Bridge
10 Brisbane
11 Clapper (accept tongue)
12 Compound
13 Turkey (accept Ottoman Empire)
14 Judaism (accept Jewish)
15 Houston
16 Tracey Ullman
17 Four-stroke
18 The Beatles
19 Lima
20 Venezuela

Round 31

1 In geography, what C is the name given to the lines on a map joining places of equal heights?

2 In which century was the X-ray discovered?

3 In film, which famous comedy duo starred in *Babes in Toyland* and *Sons of the Desert*?

4 In music, in which decade of the twentieth century was the rock band Fleetwood Mac formed?

5 In Christianity, what P is the name given to the Christian groupings that derive from the Reformation?

6 Which famous ballet company was founded in Moscow in 1776?

7 What B is a capital city on the River Danube, known as the 'White Fortress'?

8 Which character in the American TV series *Buffy the Vampire Slayer* is a werewolf, Oz or Xander?

9 What nationality was the twentieth-century composer Aaron Copland?

10 In which 1746 battle was Bonnie Prince Charlie defeated, Culloden or the Boyne?

11 What P is a single dot on a computer screen?

12 In television, Max, Bella, Fizz, Jake, Milo and Judy are all members of which popular children's programme?

13 In world geography, what country lies between Colombia and Peru on the west coast of South America?

14 In World War II, in which year was Paris liberated, 1944 or 1945?

15 Who was the lead singer of the Irish group The Pogues?

16 In UK geography, what Y is a town in Somerset known for its 400-year-old glove-making industry?

17 In television, which presenter, known for his snappy suits, hosted the programmes *The Last Resort* and *Saturday Zoo*?

18 In jazz, is Keith Jarrett a pianist or a saxophonist?

19 In Christianity, what S is the name traditionally given to the highest order of angels in the celestial hierarchy?

20 In human biology, encephalitis is the inflammation of which organ in the body?

Previous Total

( )

1,000

800

600

450

300

200

100

50

20

Banked

Total

Answers

1 Contours
2 Nineteenth
3 Laurel and Hardy (Stan Laurel and Oliver Hardy)
4 1960s (1967)
5 Protestant (*do not accept* Puritan)
6 Bolshoi
7 Belgrade (accept Beograd)
8 Oz
9 American
10 Culloden
11 Pixel (accept 'pel')
12 *The Tweenies*
13 Ecuador
14 1944
15 Shane MacGowan
16 Yeovil
17 Jonathan Ross
18 Pianist
19 Seraphim (accept seraphs)
20 The brain

Round 32

1 In which UK county is the town of Burton-upon-Trent?

2 Where on a horse's body can the frog be found?

3 Is SAS an airline of Spain or Scandinavia?

4 In maths, what size are each of the internal angles of an equilateral triangle?

5 In television, who presented *Opportunity Knocks* in the 1960s?

6 In literature, by what pen name is Charles Lutwidge Dodgson better known?

7 Which Scottish city has three cathedrals, called St Mackas, St Mary's and St Andrew's?

8 In 1911, Irving Berlin had his first hit with a song about whose ragtime band?

9 Do the nomadic Masai people live in East or West Africa?

10 In pop music, in Ken Dodd's first UK hit, he sang about love being like which musical stringed instrument?

11 In modern history, the name of the oil tanker which struck a reef off the coast of Alaska in March 1989 was the *Exxon . . .* what?

12 Which actress played the character Alex Munday in the film *Charlie's Angels* and also stars in the TV series *Ally McBeal*?

13 In which religion is the place of worship referred to as the 'Gurdwara'?

14 Which diminutive Canadian actor provided the voice for the mouse hero in the film *Stuart Little*?

15 In the animal kingdom, the goldfish is native to which country?

16 In which Shakespeare play, first performed about 1602, would you find the Greek leader Diomedes?

17 In art, what relation was the Welsh painter Gwen John to Augustus John?

18 In ancient history, the Minoans were from which island in the eastern Mediterranean?

19 In geography, the ruins of Rothsay Castle are found on which British isle?

20 According to the Hindu religion, which S was the wife of the god Rama?

Previous Total

1,000

800

600

450

300

200

100

50

20

Banked

Total

Answers

1 Staffordshire
2 On the base of the hoof (accept hoof)
3 Scandinavia
4 60 degrees
5 Hughie Green
6 Lewis Carroll
7 Aberdeen
8 Alexander's (Ragtime Band)
9 East
10 A violin
11 *Valdez*
12 Lucy Liu (Lucy Alexis Liu)
13 Sikhism
14 Michael J. Fox (Michael Andrew Fox)
15 China
16 *Troilus and Cressida*
17 Sister
18 Crete (accept Kriti/ Candia)
19 (Isle of) Bute
20 Sita

Round 33 ✓

1 In the nursery rhyme, who had lost her sheep?

2 In the human body, which organ is used for both smelling and breathing?

3 Doctor Watson was the friend of which fictional detective?

4 According to the proverb, there is no pleasure without what?

5 In the animal kingdom, what B is the name of a semi-aquatic rodent that dams streams and rivers?

6 In food, gorgonzola is a type of what?

7 How many legs does the Eiffel Tower have?

8 Polar and grizzly are types of which large mammal?

9 Which 1933 film about a huge ape ends with the words 'It was beauty killed the beast'?

10 In religion, what name is given to the Christian ceremony of initiation into the Church, usually involving the sprinkling of, or immersion in, water?

11 In nature, what colour are the breast feathers of an adult European robin?

12 What addition to postal addresses was introduced in 1959 in the UK?

13 In botany, does an aerial root begin growth above or below the ground?

14 In economics, what M is a place where coins are made?

15 How many carats is pure gold?

16 In the animal kingdom, what colour is the fur of an albino hamster?

17 What was the name of Philip Schofield's glove-puppet sidekick on the children's TV show *Going Live*?

18 What word can mean a hole in one at golf, or an unreturnable tennis serve?

19 By what shortened name is the politician Anthony Neil Wedgwood Benn more commonly known?

20 In fashion, what *B* was a device for making dresses stand out at the back?

Previous Total

1,000

800

600

450

300

200

100

50

20

Banked

Total

Answers

1 (Little) Bo-peep
2 Nose
3 Sherlock Holmes
4 Pain
5 Beaver
6 Cheese
7 Four
8 Bear
9 *King Kong*
10 Baptism (accept baptizing/ christening)
11 Red (accept orange/reddish orange/rust)
12 Post code(s)
13 Above (ground)
14 Mint (accept minting factory)
15 Twenty-four
16 White
17 Gordon the Gopher (accept Gordon)
18 Ace
19 Tony Benn
20 Bustle

Round 34

1 The 1976 biographical film *Goodbye, Norma Jean* was about which Hollywood icon?

2 A cabbage white is a variety of which insect?

3 What *P* is the name of the English football league introduced in 1992?

4 What are you said to have in your cap if you have fulfilled a personal achievement or gained an honour?

5 In nature, the terms 'queen', 'worker' and 'drone' are associated with which type of insect?

6 What name is given to the pastime of descending a steep face backwards, using a rope fixed above the climber?

7 If it takes five seconds to wash up one plate, how many minutes will it take to wash up twelve plates?

8 In music, what *H* is another name for a mouth organ?

9 In the children's novel, what kind of animal was Tarka?

10 In the song 'Hush Little Baby', what is Mother going to sing?

11 In which European city is the monument known as the Arc de Triomphe?

12 Is a columbine a plant or an animal?

13 John Hurt played the outcast John Merrick in which 1980 film?

14 In cookery, the Italian seafood dish calamari has what *S* as its principal ingredient?

15 In angling, what is the common name for the bait which is made from feathers or coloured thread?

16 In cockney rhyming slang, what is 'Rosie Lea'?

17 In which science-fiction TV series would you find Special Agent Mulder?

18 What is the BBC children's daily news programme called?

19 In transport, what is the fan-like device with rotating blades used to give forward motion to ships and aeroplanes?

20 In verse, how many stresses are there in a pentameter?

Previous Total

1,000

800

600

450

300

200

100

50

20

Banked

Total

Answers

1 Marilyn Monroe (accept Norma Jean Baker/Norma Jean Mortensen)
2 Butterfly
3 Premiership (accept Premier League)
4 Feather
5 Bee
6 Abseiling (accept *en rappel*)
7 One (minute)
8 Harmonica
9 Otter
10 A lullaby
11 Paris
12 Plant
13 *The Elephant Man*
14 Squid
15 Fly
16 Tea
17 *The X Files*
18 *Newsround*
19 Propeller (accept prop)
20 Five

1 Which James Bond star had jobs as a coffin-polisher, a milkman and a lifeguard before he found fame?

2 What *T* describes a cow's stomach prepared as food?

3 In British geography, which is further south, Swansea or Cardiff?

4 In children's literature, which character wore a tag bearing the request 'Please look after this bear – Thank you'?

5 In biology, how many lenses does each human eye have?

6 On a dartboard, which number is directly opposite the number one?

7 In the animal kingdom, is the hippopotamus a carnivore or a herbivore?

8 Which star of 1940s Hollywood movies was elected 40th president of the United States?

9 In the Bible, was Saint Bartholemew one of the apostles?

10 In nature, what *F* is a young bird that has just left the nest?

11 In the theatre, which one of the following is considered bad luck to do backstage, whistling or skipping?

12 In the cartoon, what sort of animal was superhero Hong Kong Fooey?

13 In the military, what *P* is a small firearm designed to be fired with one hand?

14 In Cornwall, what sort of food is a Tiddy Oggie? A savoury pasty or a fruit dessert?

15 Which London street, parallel to Regent Street, is famous for its exclusive tailors?

16 In commerce, what *L* is the act of ending the existence of a business or company?

17 In music, which hit song did Otis Redding record just days before his death in 1967?

18 In the human body, is the diaphragm situated above or below the liver?

19 In nature, what *T* is the common name given to a poisonous fungus that has a caplike top on the stem?

20 What was the title of the biography of *Peanuts* cartoonist Charles Schulz, published in 1989: *Good Grief* or *Not Again*?

Previous Total

1,000

800

600

450

300

200

100

50

20

Banked

Total

Answers

1 Sean Connery (Thomas Sean Connery)
2 Tripe
3 Cardiff
4 Paddington (Bear)
5 One
6 (Number) nineteen
7 Herbivore
8 Ronald Reagan
9 Yes
10 Fledgling
11 Whistling
12 Dog
13 Pistol
14 Savoury pasty
15 Savile Row
16 Liquidation
17 '(Sittin' On) The Dock of the Bay'
18 Above
19 Toadstool
20 *Good Grief*

Round 36

1 What V are organic compounds required for the maintenance of the human body's metabolic functions?

2 What is the liquid obtained by boiling meat, fish, or vegetables and used as a foundation for soup?

3 In meteorology, what S falls as a mixture of rain and partially thawed snow?

4 Which 1972 film, directed by Bob Fosse, won Liza Minnelli an Oscar for her portrayal of Sally Bowles?

5 In the British peerage, which is the higher degree of nobility, earl or marquess?

6 The poet and novelist Vikram Seth wrote the novel *A Suitable . . .* what in 1993?

7 Which Paris airport is named after a French president?

8 In fashion, aesthetes and dandies were men who dressed extravagantly in which century?

9 In British politics, which Welsh party won its first parliamentary seat in 1966?

10 What is the name of Oprah Winfrey's TV production company, Harpo or Winfo?

11 By what name is a post-mortem also known?

12 In botany, the anther and the filament in a flower together make up which S?

13 In which North African country are the cities of Fez and Marrakesh?

14 Which *K* is a small falcon with a long tail and the ability to hover before diving on its prey?

15 Does topophilia refer to intense affection or intense revulsion felt towards a place?

16 The character Rachel Wardle appears in the Dickens novel *The Pickwick . . .* what?

17 Which *A* is a theatre in London's Shaftesbury Avenue named after a Greek god?

18 In 1989, the Convention on International Trade in Endangered Species banned the trading of which substance from elephants?

19 In the animal kingdom, what insect do the English commonly call daddy-long-legs?

20 What *B* was an ancient British queen who led a rebellion through the Roman towns of Colchester, London and St Albans?

Previous Total

1,000

800

600

450

300

200

100

50

20

Banked

Total

Answers

1 Vitamins
2 Stock
3 Sleet
4 *Cabaret*
5 Marquess
6 (*A Suitable*) *Boy*
7 Charles de Gaulle
8 Nineteenth
9 Plaid Cymru (accept Welsh Nationalist Party/Nationalists)
10 Harpo
11 Autopsy
12 Stamen
13 Morocco
14 Kestrel (do not accept kite – not a falcon)
15 Affection
16 *Papers*
17 Apollo (Theatre)
18 Ivory (accept elephant tusks)
19 Crane-fly (accept *Tipula simplex*)
20 Boadicea (accept Boudicca)

Round 37

1 In 1919, John Alcock and Arthur Brown made the first non-stop flight across which ocean?

2 For what do the initials MOR stand in music?

3 What C describes the part of the human skull which encloses the brain?

4 In which continent would you find The Gambia?

5 In science, which A is an inert noble gas used in Geiger counters and household light bulbs?

6 Of which vegetable are Feltham First and Kelvedon Wonder varieties?

7 Martin and Charlie Sheen appeared together in which 1987 film set in the stockbroker world of New York City?

8 Which duo created the musical *Oklahoma* – Rodgers and Hammerstein or Gilbert and Sullivan?

9 Which Egyptian city means 'victorious' in Arabic?

10 In 1976, Britain's first ever Olympic gold medal for men's figure skating was won by John who?

11 In the animal kingdom, what P is the name given to the hide or skin of an animal with fur?

12 The Peninsular War of 1808 to 1814 was caused by which leader's invasion of Portugal and Spain?

13 The inventor Thomas Edison was born in which century?

14 The TV comedy series *Blackadder Goes Forth* was written by Richard Curtis and who?

15 Akihito became emperor of which Asian country in 1989?

16 Which US actress, who appeared in the 1990 film *Ghost*, was also the first woman to present the Academy Awards in 1994?

17 Who succeeded Bobby Charlton as the English leagues' Footballer of the Year in 1967?

18 Clint Eastwood was mayor of which Californian town, Carmel or Santa Cruz?

19 In maths, if a whole number is multiplied by itself, what do you call the product?

20 Which English royal house ruled from 1485 until the death of Elizabeth I in 1603?

Answers

1 Atlantic
2 Middle of the road
3 Cranium
4 Africa
5 Argon
6 Pea(s) (accept garden peas)
7 *Wall Street*
8 Rodgers and Hammerstein
9 Cairo
10 (John) Curry
11 Pelt
12 Napoleon (accept Napoleon the First/ Napoleon Bonaparte)
13 Nineteenth (1847)
14 Ben Elton (Benjamin Charles Elton)
15 Japan
16 Whoopi Goldberg (Caryn Elaine Johnson)
17 Jack Charlton (accept his brother)
18 Carmel
19 Square
20 Tudor

Previous Total

1,000
800
600
450
300
200
100
50
20

Banked

Total

Round 38

1 What was the name of the 1980s TV series about the formative years of the characters from *Last of the Summer Wine*?

2 In language, what A is a German word for an emotional sense of anxiety without a specific cause?

3 In which US city was Martin Luther King born?

4 Which dame of the British theatre was married to her *Prime of Miss Jean Brodie* co-star, Sir Robert Stephens?

5 The name of the famous American childcare author was Doctor Benjamin . . . what?

6 In pop music, from which Scandinavian country did the band Ace of Base originate?

7 In nature, the resin of the terebinth pine was the original source of which DIY product, beginning with *T*?

8 What type of camera, invented by George Eastman, first went on sale in the USA in 1900?

9 In maths, what is eighteen multiplied by four?

10 In industry, what S is the name of the process by which metals such as iron are extracted from their ores?

11 Tiger Woods won the 2000 British Open on which Scottish golf course?

12 What was the name of the charter drawn up in 1215 and regarded as the basis for civil liberties in England?

13 Which south-eastern state of America is home to Palm Beach and Daytona Beach?

14 Which famous basketball star took over as owner of the ice hockey team the Washington Capitals in the year 2000?

15 In science, what *S* are formed when an acid reacts with a base?

16 George Peppard appeared as the character Paul Varjak in which 1961 film starring Audrey Hepburn?

17 In which English county is the cathedral city of Ely?

18 In science, what colour is the element sulphur when solid?

19 Which eastern state of America is home to Kennedy Space Center's Spaceport USA?

20 What is the name of the late-night music show presented by Jools Holland since 1992?

Previous Total

1,000

800

600

450

300

200

100

50

20

Banked

Total

Answers

1 *First of the Summer Wine*
2 Angst
3 Atlanta
4 (Dame) Maggie Smith (Margaret Natalie Smith)
5 Spock
6 Sweden
7 Turpentine
8 Brownie
9 Seventy-two
10 Smelting
11 St Andrews
12 Magna Carta
13 Florida
14 Michael Jordan (Michael Jeffrey Jordan)
15 Salts
16 *Breakfast at Tiffany's*
17 Cambridgeshire
18 Yellow (accept greenish yellow)
19 Florida
20 *Later with Jools Holland*

Round 39

1 According to the first line of Shakespeare's *Twelfth Night*, music might be the food of what?

2 In which sport are the Ashes a trophy?

3 In the TV series *Only Fools and Horses*, to which character did Del Boy usually say 'You plonker'?

4 The traditional wish of good luck among performers in the theatre is 'Break a . . .' what?

5 In the nursery rhyme, to which English city did Doctor Foster go?

6 In which game of chance, using numbers between one and ninety, might a player shout 'House!'?

7 Which annual world beauty contest was held at the Millennium Dome in November 2000?

8 'Reef' and 'granny' are types of what *K*?

9 Which famous duo won Olympic gold for figure skating in 1984, performing their routine to Ravel's *Bolero*?

10 How is the *Felis catus* more commonly known?

11 According to the proverb, 'Fools rush in' where who fear to tread?

12 Which lizard changes colour to hide from predators?

13 The three-foot-tall US entertainer Charles Sherwood Stratton was more commonly known as 'Tom . . .' what?

14 In music, what *V* is the alto member of the violin family that is longer than a violin and with a deeper tone?

15 In television, Lisa Kudrow plays the character Phoebe in which American comedy series?

16 Which chemical element, with the symbol Cl, is used as a disinfectant in swimming pools?

17 Which popular pastime from Japan takes its name from the Japanese words for 'empty' and 'orchestra'?

18 If you buy four apples, twelve oranges and three pears, how many pieces of fruit do you have?

19 In the animal kingdom, does the hamster carry its food back to the nest in a cheek pouch or stomach pouch?

20 In pop music, which letter of the alphabet completes the name of this disco band: Boney . . . what?

Previous Total
1,000
800
600
450
300
200
100
50
20
Banked
Total

Answers

1 Love
2 Cricket
3 Rodney (his brother)
4 (Break a) leg
5 Gloucester
6 Bingo (accept Housey Housey/ Lotto)
7 Miss World
8 Knot(s)
9 Torvill and Dean (Jayne Torvill and Christopher Colin Dean)
10 Domestic cat (accept cat/house cat)
11 Angels
12 Kameleon (accept Anole)
13 (Tom) Thumb
14 Viola
15 *Friends*
16 Chlorine
17 Karaoke
18 Nineteen
19 Cheek (pouch)
20 M

Round 40

1 In ancient history, Attila the what attacked the eastern frontier of the Roman Empire in the fifth century AD?

2 In which sport have Joe Johnson and Dennis Taylor been world champions?

3 In food, what type of vegetable is a Maris Piper?

4 In the 1960s and 1970s TV comedy series *On The Buses*, was Reg Varney's character, Stan, a bus driver or bus conductor?

5 A ruminant is a mammal that chews the what?

6 Complete the title of this Matt Damon and Ben Affleck film: *Good Will . . .* what?

7 Which Welsh poet and playwright's dying words were reputed to be: 'I've had eighteen straight whiskeys. I think that's the record'?

8 What is the full name of the medical organisation known as the BMA?

9 Which TV comedian played Kevin the Teenager in the film *Kevin and Perry Go Large*?

10 Multiply the number of days in the week by the number of months in the year.

11 In the UK, what is the name of the road safety code that teaches children to Stop, Look, Listen and Think?

12 A pointer is a breed of which animal?

13 In travel, the M8 links Glasgow with which other major Scottish city?

14 In which city is the Kremlin?

15 Which pop star admitted in November 2000 to going on a two-million-pound spending spree following a record deal in 1996?

16 In the Bible, Lot's wife was turned into what?

17 In the 1980s TV series, which Sue Townsend character confessed his love for Pandora in his *Secret Diary*?

18 What was the common name for the Community Charge brought in by Margaret Thatcher in 1989 to 1990?

19 In biology, which word is used to describe animals with backbones?

20 What *P* is the name given to a vertical cave system, or a circular hole in the bedrock of a river?

Previous Total

1,000

800

600

450

300

200

100

50

20

Banked

Total

Answers

1 (Attila the) Hun
2 Snooker
3 Potato
4 (Bus) driver
5 Cud
6 *Hunting*
7 Dylan Thomas (Dylan Marlais Thomas)
8 British Medical Association
9 Harry Enfield
10 Eighty-four
11 The Green Cross Code
12 Dog
13 Edinburgh
14 Moscow
15 (Sir) Elton John (Reginald Kenneth Dwight)
16 A pillar of salt
17 Adrian Mole
18 Poll Tax
19 Vertebrates
20 Pothole

Round 41

1 The YHA is an organisation that provides accommodation for travellers. For what do the letters YHA stand?

2 In classical music, is an aria a solo vocal piece or a group orchestral piece?

3 Erich Veiss was the real name of which escapologist?

4 In which American TV series did David Hasselhoff play the lifeguard Mitch Buchannon?

5 What F are long-legged birds, famed for their pink-tinged plumage, that live entirely by filter feeding?

6 In literature, does the Cheshire Cat or the Cornish Cat appear in *Alice's Adventures in Wonderland*?

7 Which V is a man-made cellulose fibre derived from wood pulp?

8 What is the name of the wax secreted by worker bees in a hive that is used to construct their combs?

9 In handicrafts, what would you be doing if you were forming a moss-stitch or rib-stitch?

10 In modern literature, what was the name of Alan Bennett's series of six monologues published in 1988?

11 Which British singer, who was born Elaine Bookbinder, had hits including 'Pearls A Singer' and 'Sunshine After The Rain'?

12 Which insect is said to have got its name because of an ancient belief that it crawled into the ears of sleeping people?

13 From which country in the UK did the outlaw Rob Roy come?

14 Which English waif supermodel from Croydon was discovered at the age of fourteen at JFK Airport?

15 Who was the Greek god of love?

16 Name the giant radioactive dinosaur that first appeared in a Japanese film in 1954 and has since been the subject of films and cartoon TV series?

17 Is the Docklands development in east or west London?

18 What *T* is the cold region in which mostly lichens, mosses and small shrubs survive?

19 In the Bible, is the Book of Amos in the Old or New Testament?

20 What *A* is a medical name for baldness?

Previous Total
1,000
800
600
450
300
200
100
50
20
Banked
Total

Answers

1 Youth Hostel Association	**11** Elkie Brooks
2 Solo vocal piece	**12** Earwig
3 Harry Houdini	**13** Scotland
4 *Baywatch* (accept *Baywatch Hawaii*)	**14** Kate Moss
5 Flamingos	**15** Eros (*do not accept* Cupid)
6 Cheshire Cat	**16** Godzilla (accept Gojira)
7 Viscose	**17** East
8 Beeswax	**18** Tundra
9 Knitting	**19** Old
10 *Talking Heads*	**20** Alopecia

Round 42

1 The song 'No Woman, No Cry' was the first UK top 40 hit for which famous singer?

2 On television, what is the name of BBC2's flagship science documentary series that has been running for thirty-five years?

3 In nutrition, what R is another word for dietary fibre?

4 In geography, Hugh Town is the capital of which group of islands in the UK?

5 In science, which K is the noble gas that is used inside fluorescent tubes?

6 In literature, was Alfred Tennyson an English or an American poet?

7 What S is a Scandinavian country famous for the salmon dish gravlax?

8 Name the 1990s TV satire show starring David Baddiel and Rob Newman that took its name from a television moral crusader?

9 In nature, hawthorn blossom is traditionally named after which month of the year?

10 Who directed the 1954 film *Dial M for Murder*?

11 Who was Frank Bruno's American opponent in the first televised pay-per-view fight shown in Britain in 1996?

12 In fishing, is the brown trout a game fish or a coarse fish?

13 In food, Palestine soup is made from a vegetable known as the Jerusalem what?

Previous Total

14 Fritz Kreisler was a twentieth-century virtuoso on which stringed instrument?

15 In politics, in what year did the Maastricht Treaty come into effect, 1993 or 1995?

16 In nature, cocksfoot and Yorkshire fog are both types of which plant?

17 In history, the English king who founded Westminster Abbey was known as Edward the what?

18 In Greek literature, what *L* is the birthplace of the female Greek lyric poet Sappho?

19 In pop music, which of the following is *not* one of Michael Jackson's sisters: Rebbie, Janet or Deborah?

20 In medicine, what C is an acute bacterial infection of the small intestine which is mainly contracted from contaminated water?

1,000
800
600
450
300
200
100
50
20

Banked

Total

Answers

1 Bob Marley
2 *Horizon*
3 Roughage
4 Scilly Isles
5 Krypton
6 English
7 Sweden
8 *The Mary Whitehouse Experience*
9 May
10 Alfred Hitchcock
11 Mike Tyson
12 Game fish
13 Artichoke
14 Violin
15 1993
16 Grasses (accept grass)
17 Confessor (accept Saint/Saint Edward)
18 Lesbos
19 Deborah
20 Cholera

Round 43

1 Did Edward VIII abdicate before or after World War II?

2 In the children's book *The Lion, the Witch and the Wardrobe*, which character was the first to reach Narnia: Peter, Susan or Lucy?

3 Toronto is the capital city of which Canadian province?

4 What is the full name of the country known as the UAE?

5 Name the musical written by Pete Townshend and The Who about a deaf, dumb and blind boy?

6 In which US state is the city of Houston?

7 What *E* is the Baltic country whose capital is Tallinn?

8 According to St John's Gospel, what was 'In the beginning' with God?

9 In medicine, which *U* is a scanning technique used in obstetrics to examine a foetus?

10 In biology, what gas is the main waste product of respiration in air-breathing animals?

11 In nature, 'red', 'Norway' and 'sugar' are all varieties of which tree whose leaf features on the Canadian flag?

12 DVLA stands for the Driving and Vehicle . . . what?

13 During World War II, the American Boeing B-17 was known as the Flying . . . what?

14 Which actress plays the orange-haired character Linda La Hughes in the TV sitcom *Gimme, Gimme, Gimme*?

15 In which series of comedy films did the actor Herbert Lom play Chief Inspector Dreyfus?

16 In the animal kingdom, what *L* is a short-tailed member of the cat family that inhabits the forests of Eurasia and North America?

17 In which century did Richard Sheridan write the play *The Rivals*?

18 In world geography, name either of the two countries that the River Ganges runs through.

19 In Iranian mythology, was Tishtrya the god of rain or snow?

20 What *B* is a Christian religious order, founded by St Benedict, which places the emphasis on prayer, work and the reading of holy books?

Previous Total

1,000

800

600

450

300

200

100

50

20

Banked

Total

Answers

1 Before	**12** Licensing Agency
2 Lucy	**13** Fortress
3 Ontario	**14** Kathy Burke
4 United Arab Emirates	**15** *Pink Panther*
5 *Tommy*	**16** Lynx
6 Texas	**17** Eighteenth century
7 Estonia	(1775)
8 The word	**18** India/Bangladesh
9 Ultrasound	**19** Rain
10 Carbon dioxide	**20** Benedictines (accept
11 Maple	Benedictine)

Round 44

1 Who designed an allegedly unpickable lock in 1818 to prevent burglaries at a naval dock, Jeremiah Chubb or Linus Yale?

2 What title did Hitler take as leader of Germany in imitation of Mussolini's title of Il Duce?

3 In sport, the Highs-man Trophy is presented to the best college player in what American sport?

4 An exothermic reaction is a reaction that gives off what?

5 Which national newspaper was founded in London in 1785 as the *Daily Universal Register*?

6 In car engines, what device ignites the petrol–air mixture in the cylinder?

7 What is the French fashion term meaning 'ready to wear'?

8 In which American state is the ski resort of Vail?

9 Umberto II was the last reigning monarch of which European country, now a republic?

10 Which Y is a plant also known as Adam's Needle?

11 In the TV comedy *The Royle Family*, which actress plays the part of Denise?

12 Sharon Stone was nominated for an Academy Award in which 1995 gangster film directed by Martin Scorsese?

13 What T is the title of the opera composed by Puccini that was first performed in 1900?

14 What S is Africa's largest country by area?

15 Which member of the Beatles sang solo on the tracks 'With a Little Help From My Friends' and 'Octopus's Garden'?

16 Which Suffolk town's racecourse is called the Rowley Mile, after Charles II's favourite horse?

17 In science, the study of the planet Earth as a whole is known as what science?

18 With which Swedish-born actress did Humphrey Bogart appear in the 1942 romantic film *Casablanca*?

19 What R is a small historic county in the East Midlands that has one of the largest artificial reservoirs in the UK?

20 In film, Jack Nicholson won the Best Actor Oscar for which 1975 film?

Previous Total
⬭
1,000
800
600
450
300
200
100
50
20
Banked
⬭
⬭
⬭
⬭
⬭
Total
⬭

Answers

1 Jeremiah Chubb	**11** Caroline Aherne
2 Führer (Der Führer)	**12** *Casino*
3 American football (accept football)	**13** *Tosca*
4 Heat (thermal energy)	**14** The Sudan
5 *The Times*	**15** Ringo Starr (accept Richard Starky)
6 The spark plug (accept sparking-plug)	**16** Newmarket
7 *Prêt-à-porter*	**17** Earth science (accept geoscience)
8 Colorado	**18** Ingrid Bergman
9 Italy	**19** Rutland
10 Yucca plant	**20** *One Flew Over the Cuckoo's Nest*

Round 45

1 In the nursery rhyme 'Hickory Dickory Dock', what ran up the clock?

2 Which cereal or grain is traditionally thrown at a wedding?

3 How much is a first-class stamp?

4 Complete the title of this song by Ian Dury and the Blockheads: 'Hit Me With Your . . .'.

5 Which fruit grows in bunches known as hands?

6 Which Scottish dish traditionally consists of the stuffed stomach of a sheep?

7 In which UK country was the author and poet Dylan Thomas born?

8 An uncontrollable action of natural forces that cannot be foreseen is known as an act of . . . what?

9 In food, Harry Ramsden founded what kind of restaurant in 1928?

10 In the animal kingdom, can an emu fly?

11 In language, which fruit is an unwanted third person when lovers are together?

12 In J. M. Barrie's *Peter Pan*, what was the name of the fairy?

13 In medicine, what P is an electronic device used to correct an abnormal or irregular heart rate?

14 Which comedian's catchphrase was 'Just like that'?

15 In DIY, anaglypta and vymura are both types of what?

16 In clothing, what is an espadrille?

17 In the TV soap *EastEnders*, what is the character name of Dot Cotton's son?

18 Traditionally, a string of what food is linked with the puppets Punch and Judy?

19 In golf, which is a better score, an eagle or a birdie?

20 What is the name of the immature form of a frog or toad?

Previous Total

1,000

800

600

450

300

200

100

50

20

Banked

Total

Answers

1 Mouse	**10** No
2 Rice	**11** Gooseberry
3 Twenty-seven pence	**12** Tinkerbell
4 'Rhythm Stick'	**13** Pacemaker
5 Banana(s)	**14** Tommy Cooper
6 Haggis	**15** Wallpaper
7 Wales	**16** Shoe (accept
8 (Act of) God	footwear/sandal)
9 Fish and chips	**17** Nick (Cotton)
(accept fish/	**18** Sausages
chippie/chip shop/	**19** Eagle
seafood)	**20** Tadpole

Round 46

1 In television, which British comedian and presenter hosted the programme *Bob Says Opportunity Knocks*?

2 Flute, schooner and tumbler are all types of what?

3 Which female South African athlete became famous for running with bare feet?

4 In sport, how many events are there in a decathlon?

5 What is the name of the Hunchback of Notre Dame?

6 Old Maid and Rummy are both types of what?

7 Complete the title of this Richard Burton film: *The Spy Who Came In From the . . .* what?

8 In cookery, what G is the name of the Mexican dish mainly consisting of mashed avocado mixed with lemon or lime juice and various seasonings?

9 What B is a tough but lightweight wood, often used for making model aeroplanes?

10 Which Hollywood actor took the role of Forrest Gump in the 1994 film of the same name?

11 In nature, what C is the name given to the small divisions of a garlic bulb?

12 In which country was pop star Kylie Minogue born?

13 By what name is the system of flyovers on the M6 near Birmingham more commonly known?

14 In biology, the hammer is the common name for a small bone found in which part of the human body?

15 In science, what M is one of the elements used to make white-coloured fireworks?

16 In television, which American spin-off from the series *Cheers* stars Kelsey Grammer as the host of a radio phone-in show?

17 How many days are there in the month of April?

18 In pop music, on which Michael Jackson album did the song 'Billie Jean' first appear, *Bad* or *Thriller*?

19 Which dance traditionally begins and ends the show at the Moulin Rouge in Paris?

20 In Christianity, what G is the geographical region where Jesus grew up in the town of Nazareth?

Previous Total

1,000

800

600

450

300

200

100

50

20

Banked

Total

Answers

1 Bob Monkhouse
2 (Drinking) glasses
3 Zola Budd
4 Ten
5 Quasimodo
6 Card game(s)
7 *Cold*
8 Guacamole
9 Balsa (accept balsa-wood)
10 Tom Hanks
11 Clove
12 Australia
13 Spaghetti Junction
14 Middle ear (accept ear)
15 Magnesium
16 *Frasier*
17 Thirty
18 *Thriller*
19 Can-Can
20 Galilee

1 In science, what name is given to the downward force acting on a free-falling object?

2 Set in Ambridge, what is the longest-running radio drama series in Britain?

3 In the animal kingdom, how many eggs does a flamingo usually lay each year, one or six?

4 In education, for what do the letters NUT stand?

5 How much would it cost to buy a 70p bus ticket every day from Monday to Sunday inclusive?

6 Is water an organic or inorganic molecule?

7 What was the name of Judy Garland's character in the 1939 film *The Wizard of Oz*?

8 What kind of creature is a lamprey?

9 In 1954, Roger Bannister was the first athlete to run what distance in a recorded time of under four minutes?

10 What A is a city in South Australia, situated at the base of the Mount Lofty Ranges?

11 In the animal kingdom, what is the name given to a species of beetle whose larvae feed on dung?

12 In science, what C describes the change in state of a substance from a gas to a liquid?

13 What nickname was given to young women in the 1920s who bobbed their hair and wore shapeless dresses: flappers or bobbers?

14 In the military, what *A* is a collective term for firearms too heavy to be carried?

15 Which Irish pop star tore up a picture of the pope, on US TV in 1993?

16 In Britain, what name is given to the poet who is a salaried member of the British royal household?

17 In which year did the Wright brothers make their first sustained powered flight: 1903 or 1912?

18 A joint in which a rounded end lies in a concave shape is a ball-and-. . . what joint?

19 In geography, what *P* is a strip of land surrounded by water on three sides?

20 Is the martial art aikido Chinese or Japanese in origin?

Previous Total

1,000

800

600

450

300

200

100

50

20

Banked

Total

Answers

1 Gravity
2 *The Archers*
3 One
4 National Union of Teachers
5 £4.90 (accept 490p/four-ninety)
6 Inorganic
7 Dorothy
8 Fish (accept jawless fish)
9 A mile
10 Adelaide
11 Dung beetle
12 Condensation
13 Flappers
14 Artillery
15 Sinead O'Connor
16 Poet Laureate
17 1903
18 Socket (accept ball-and-socket joint/ enarthrosis)
19 Peninsula
20 Japanese

Round 48

1 In the animal kingdom, how many toes does a hedgehog have: four or five?

2 Which European capital city is served by the airports at Orly and Le Bourget?

3 In geography, which is the world's smallest ocean?

4 In finance, what *S* is the duty levied on certain legal transactions including share-dealing and the purchase of property?

5 In sport, do Leeds Rhinos play Rugby League or Rugby Union?

6 In which 1970s and 1980s US TV sitcom was Arnold Jackson's catchphrase 'Whatchoo talking about, Willis'?

7 What type of vehicle is a Chinese junk?

8 In geography, infiltration is the process by which *what* enters rocks or soil?

9 Which athlete was disqualified from the 1988 Olympic 100 metres final for testing positive in a drugs test?

10 In UK politics, whose ceremonial address opens every session of parliament?

11 Which Charles Dickens book features the characters Meg and Toby Veck: *The Chimes* or *Oliver Twist*?

12 In nature, what name is given to flowering plants that live and die within a single year?

13 In which English county is Epping Forest?

14 In television, which comedy drama was filmed in the village of Avoca in Ireland's County Wicklow?

15 In which Scottish city could you visit the People's Palace Museum and the Burrell Collection?

16 Which Middle Eastern country used to be known as Persia?

17 In film, which actor played Butch in the 1969 western *Butch Cassidy and the Sundance Kid*?

18 In which film series did the characters Martin Riggs and Roger Murtaugh appear?

19 Who won the Nobel Peace Prize in 1989 for his non-violent resistance to China?

20 In geography, is the Suez Canal a natural waterway?

Previous Total

1,000
800
600
450
300
200
100
50
20

Banked

Total

Answers

1 Five	**11** *The Chimes*
2 Paris	**12** Annual(s)
3 Arctic (Ocean)	**13** Essex
4 Stamp (duty)	**14** *Ballykissangel*
5 Rugby League	**15** Glasgow
6 *Diff'rent Strokes*	**16** Iran
7 Boat (accept ship)	**17** Paul Newman
8 Water	**18** *Lethal Weapon*
9 Ben Johnson	**19** Dalai Lama
10 The monarch (accept the Queen/the Sovereign)	**20** No

Round 49

1 In television, what was the first name of David Jason's character in the sitcom *Open All Hours*?

2 Who played Detective Lieutenant Frank Bullitt in the 1968 film *Bullitt*?

3 In which country is the pula the currency: Botswana or Mozambique?

4 In maths, if a whole number is multiplied by itself and then by itself again, what do you call the product?

5 In boxing, at which category of weight has Lennox Lewis won world titles?

6 Which city is further south: Cape Town in South Africa, or Perth in Australia?

7 In theatre, which Welsh actor made his Broadway debut in the play *Equus* in 1974?

8 Which royal society, founded in 1830, is dedicated to expanding knowledge of the world through expeditions?

9 In politics, which former chancellor resigned in 1993 following the withdrawal of the pound from the European Monetary System?

10 In film, which Hollywood icon of the 1950s appeared as the character Jor-El in the 1978 film *Superman*?

11 Complete the title of this play by Eugene O'Neill from 1946: *The Iceman . . . what?*

12 In which continent is Siberia?

13 What is the common name given to the clavicle bone?

14 Who sang the 1979 British number one hit single 'We Don't Talk Any More'?

15 In which Central European country would the native language be Magyar?

16 Does 'fission' mean joining or splitting apart?

17 In music, the song 'Summertime' is from which Gershwin opera?

18 Which former football player's film roles have included the characters Big Chris and Bullet Tooth Tony?

19 In science, which of the noble gases is used in airships?

20 In music, Australian A. B. Paterson is most famous for writing which traditional Australian song?

Previous Total
◯

| 1,000 |
| 800 |
| 600 |
| 450 |
| 300 |
| 200 |
| 100 |
| 50 |
| 20 |

Banked

◯
◯
◯
◯
◯

Total

◯

Answers

1 Granville (Granville Arkwright)
2 Steve McQueen (Terence Steven McQueen)
3 Botswana
4 Cube
5 Heavyweight
6 Cape Town
7 (Sir) Anthony Hopkins (Philip Anthony Hopkins)
8 Royal Geographical Society
9 Norman Lamont
10 Marlon Brando (Marlon Brando Junior)
11 (*The Iceman*) *Cometh*
12 Asia
13 Collar bone
14 Cliff Richard (Harry Roger Webb)
15 Hungary
16 Splitting apart
17 *Porgy and Bess*
18 Vinnie Jones
19 Helium
20 'Waltzing Matilda'

Round 50

1 Which television drama series starred Lenny Henry as head teacher Ian George?

2 In geography, the city of Chester lies on which river?

3 In which religion are the two festive days in the year referred to as Ids?

4 In which former British colony was the game of snooker invented in 1875?

5 In the USA, what is the state capital of Arizona?

6 What B was the name of the first purpose-built motor-racing track in the world?

7 In pop music, where was the singer Leonard Cohen born: America or Canada?

8 In nature, is the devil's coach horse a beetle or a caterpillar?

9 If a scooter travels 15 kilometres in half an hour, what is its average speed per hour?

10 In which 1999 Oscar-winning film did Kevin Spacey and Annette Bening appear as Lester and Carolyn Burnham?

11 In history, which 1485 battle ended the Wars of the Roses: Bosworth Field or Stamford Bridge?

12 What G describes an eighteenth- and nineteenth-century style of novel dealing with tales of the macabre and supernatural?

13 The Taj Mahal was built in which century?

14 In verse, what is the name given to a pair of rhyming lines?

15 In music, who duetted with Neil Tennant on the Pet Shop Boys' hit song 'What Have I Done To Deserve This'?

16 In electronics, the three points on a British plug are live, neutral and what?

17 Which actor played the title role in the 1939 film *Goodbye Mr Chips*: Robert Donat or Charles Laughton?

18 *Alf* was a hit album for which female artist in 1985?

19 In 1990, who was elected chancellor of the reunified Germany?

20 In sport, in which country was England cricketer Graeme Hick born?

Previous Total

1,000

800

600

450

300

200

100

50

20

Banked

Total

Answers

1 Hope and Glory	**12** Gothic
2 (River) Dee	**13** Seventeenth
3 Islam (accept	(1631–53)
Muslim/	**14** A couplet
Mohammedanism)	**15** Dusty Springfield
4 India	(Mary Isabel
5 Phoenix	Catherine Bernadette
6 Brooklands	O'Brien)
7 Canada	**16** Earth
8 Beetle	**17** Robert Donat
9 30 km/h	**18** Alison Moyet
10 American Beauty	**19** Helmut Kohl
11 Bosworth Field	**20** Zimbabwe

Round 51

1 In science, what *H* is a device used to measure the density of a liquid?

2 For which UK charity organisation is the avocet bird the symbol?

3 The Clifton Suspension Bridge spans which gorge in Bristol?

4 Was the guitar legend Jimi Hendrix right or left-handed?

5 In modern literature, which American novelist, associated with the beat generation, wrote *Junkie* and *Naked Lunch*?

6 Which of these martial arts is *not* in the Olympics: judo, karate or tae kwon do?

7 In religion, is polytheism the belief in and worship of one god or many gods?

8 In the Bible, to whom did God speak from a burning bush?

9 In which southern US state is the Space and Rocket Center in Huntsville?

10 Which *K* is a famous national park in the north-east of South Africa?

11 Who wrote the musical *Blood Brothers*?

12 In literature, which Henry James novel features the story of Isabel Archer?

13 Which French term describes a small work of art, like a miniature painting, snuff box or statuette?

14 What type of baby food was first marketed by Henri Nestlé in 1876 in Switzerland?

15 In the animal kingdom, mammals that are ungulates share which anatomical feature?

16 In literature, which French author wrote *Twenty Thousand Leagues Under the Sea*?

17 In music, Kurt Cobain was lead singer with which rock band founded in 1988?

18 In a survey of 500 farmers, 230 had livestock, so how many did not?

19 Which composer wrote the opera *Fidelio*?

20 In the novel *Brideshead Revisited*, at which university did Charles meet Sebastian?

Previous Total

1,000

800

600

450

300

200

100

50

20

Banked

Total

Answers

1 Hydrometer
2 RSPB (Royal Society for the Protection of Birds)
3 Avon (Gorge)
4 Left-handed
5 William Burroughs (William Seward Burroughs)
6 Karate
7 Many (gods)
8 Moses
9 Alabama
10 Kruger
11 Willy Russell
12 *The Portrait of a Lady*
13 Objet d'art
14 Powdered milk
15 Hooves
16 Jules Verne
17 Nirvana
18 270
19 (Ludwig van) Beethoven
20 Oxford

Round 52

1 What is Popeye the Sailor Man's favourite food?

2 According to legend, what B is a household cleaning implement that supposedly enables a witch to fly?

3 With which sport would you associate Joe Frazier?

4 In the animal kingdom, what is the name given to a group of elephants?

5 In human biology, what name is given to the ridged patterns on the fingertips?

6 In science, what B is a substance that neutralises an acid to form salt and water?

7 In pop music, complete the title of this 1989 Phil Collins single: 'Another Day in . . .' what?

8 Which type of meat comes in streaky, smoked and unsmoked varieties?

9 In medicine, what S is a device commonly used by doctors to listen to sounds within the organs of a patient's body?

10 In the *Mr Men* stories, what colour was Mr Happy?

11 In food, what name is given to the sweet, yellow, crescent-shaped fruit that grows in tropical regions and can be eaten raw?

12 In the TV comedy series *Only Fools and Horses*, what was Derek Trotter's nickname?

13 In clothing, what S is the name given to the pouch worn in front of a Scottish kilt?

14 In humans, the nape is the common term for the back of what part of the body?

15 Which picture playing card ranks below the king but above the jack in most card games?

16 In children's television, which pink, knitted, mouse-like aliens communicated in high-pitched whistles and lived under dustbin lids?

17 With which sport would you associate John Parrott?

18 According to the proverb, 'Where there's . . .' what, 'there's brass'?

19 Traditionally, which festival is celebrated on 31 October?

20 Complete the title of the following American TV comedy series: *Mork and . . .* who?

Previous Total

1,000

800

600

450

300

200

100

50

20

Banked

Total

Answers

1 Spinach
2 Broomstick (accept broom/besom)
3 Boxing
4 Herd
5 Fingerprints
6 Base
7 Paradise
8 Bacon (accept pork)
9 Stethoscope
10 Yellow
11 Banana (*do not* accept plantain – not sweet and must be cooked)
12 Del Boy (accept Del)
13 Sporran
14 Neck
15 The queen
16 *The Clangers*
17 Snooker
18 Muck
19 Hallowe'en (accept All Hallows' Eve)
20 *Mindy*

Round 53

1 What A is a puzzle whereby letters of a word are rearranged to form a new word or phrase?

2 In maths, add the number of legs on a spider to the number of signs of the zodiac.

3 In food, haricot, runner and broad are all types of what?

4 What is the name of the pastime in which engraved designs on brasses are transferred onto paper using coloured wax?

5 Complete the title of this children's story by Hans Christian Andersen: 'The Ugly . . .' what?

6 The dog and burnet are species of which sweet-scented British wild flower?

7 In film, what C is a small but significant role often played by a famous actor?

8 In pop music, which band won a Brit Award in 1996 for the album *What's the Story, Morning Glory*?

9 Which Welsh actress starred in the films *The Mask of Zorro* and *Entrapment*?

10 In nature, what colour is a starling's egg, blue or white?

11 The TV medical drama *Holby City* is a spin-off from which long-running series?

12 What S is a material used in footwear and clothing, made by buffing the flesh side of a tanned animal hide?

13 Which board game shares its name with a tragic Shakespearean character?

14 Complete the title of the 1993 film starring Robert Redford and Demi Moore: *Indecent . . .* what?

15 Does an epilogue come at the beginning or end of a play?

16 What *P*, derived from German, describes an invisible spirit which makes its presence known by noise or the movement of objects?

17 On a paper round, a boy delivers papers to 50 houses per hour. How many houses does he deliver to in his two-and-a-half-hour shift?

18 Complete the title of the 1994 film starring Jim Carrey: *Dumb and . . .* what?

19 In television, which BBC science-fiction series featured sea devils and giant maggots?

20 In UK customs, by what other name is a beefeater known?

Previous Total

1,000

800

600

450

300

200

100

50

20

Banked

Total

Answers

1 Anagram	**12** Suede
2 20	**13** Othello
3 Bean (accept legume)	**14** *Proposal*
4 Brass rubbing	**15** End
5 '(The Ugly) Duckling'	**16** Poltergeist
6 Rose	**17** 125
7 Cameo	**18** *Dumber*
8 Oasis	**19** *Doctor Who*
9 Catherine Zeta-Jones	**20** Yeoman of the Guard (accept Warder of the Tower of London)
10 Blue	
11 *Casualty*	

Round 54

1 In science, is a cathode a negative or a positive electrode?

2 What M is a type of sculpture that has suspended elements, or is itself suspended, so that it may move?

3 In the military, what do the initials RM stand for?

4 In politics, the four founders of the SDP were originally members of which party?

5 What O is an anise-flavoured liqueur from Greece?

6 Which major city is served by an airport with the location code SYD?

7 In UK geography, which T is the chief river in the midlands?

8 What is the common name for the blood-sucking insects that infest houses and particularly beds?

9 In politics, what E is the process of appointing someone to public office by voting?

10 In clothing, over what part of the body is a yashmak worn?

11 Does the pistil of a flower bear seeds or pollen?

12 What name is given to the young of a zebra?

13 In geography, Gouda is a town in which European country?

14 In music, if a person is described as singing flat, are they singing higher or lower than the required pitch?

15 In television, Sid Snot was a character created by which controversial DJ and comedian?

16 In history, who was crowned emperor of France in 1804?

17 Are the Abbey Gardens in Tresco situated on the Channel Islands or the Isles of Scilly?

18 In fashion, what *T* is a person who makes, repairs and alters clothing?

19 In sport, which male British tennis player became the National Junior Champion in 1992?

20 In theatre, which British dramatist wrote the play *Fanny's First Play* in 1911: George Bernard Shaw or George Orwell?

Answers

1 Negative
2 Mobile
3 Royal Marines
4 Labour (Party)
5 Ouzo
6 Sydney
7 (River) Trent
8 Bed bugs (accept Cimicidae)
9 Election
10 Face
11 Seeds
12 Foal
13 The Netherlands (accept Holland)
14 Lower
15 Kenny Everett
16 Napoleon (Napoleon Bonaparte)
17 Isles of Scilly
18 Tailor
19 Tim Henman (Timothy Henry Henman)
20 George Bernard Shaw

Round 55

1 Which state leads the American nation in the production of citrus fruits?

2 In history, the 1773 American protest against the British tax on tea is commonly known as what?

3 In human biology, which organ do the coronary arteries supply with blood?

4 The Downhill, Super-G and Giant Slalom World Cup are competitions in which winter sport?

5 In UK geography, what *W* is a city on the River Severn?

6 In biology, what name is given to the early stage in the development of an animal after fertilisation of an ovum and before birth?

7 Which 1970s UK TV sitcom features the characters Mr La-di-da Gunner Graham and Gloria?

8 Which city founded a university first: Oxford or Paris?

9 Which country did the Beatles visit for the first time in 1964?

10 In music, which member of the Sex Pistols went on to form Public Image Ltd?

11 In politics, what *E* is a government-imposed suspension of trade with another country?

12 Valentina Tereshkova became the first woman to go where in 1963?

13 In history, what *M* was the name given to the heavy flat stones used to grind grain to a powder?

14 In science, does a convex surface curve inwards or outwards?

15 In pop music, which 1980s band, with a fruity name, comprised Keren Woodward, Sarah Dallin and Siobhan Fahey?

16 In geography, what *N* is the largest country in Central America?

17 In economics, the difference between a country's income and its expenditure abroad is known as the 'balance of . . .' what?

18 Opposite which actor did Donna Reed appear in the 1946 film *It's a Wonderful Life*?

19 In theatre, what is the surname of Sir Cameron . . ., the British producer born in 1946?

20 The Cree are a native Indian people of which country?

Answers

1 Florida
2 Boston Tea Party
3 Heart
4 Skiing (alpine skiing)
5 Worcester
6 Embryo
7 *It Ain't Half Hot Mum*
8 Paris
9 United States (accept US/USA/United States of America/America)
10 Johnny Rotten (accept John Lydon/John Joseph Lydon)
11 Embargo
12 Space
13 Millstone
14 Outwards
15 Bananarama
16 Nicaragua
17 Payments
18 Jimmy Stewart (James Maitland Stewart)
19 Mackintosh
20 Canada

Round 56

1 With which religion is the Tripitaka Scripture associated?

2 In the UK, is Torbay a district in Devon, Cornwall or Somerset?

3 What term referring to the 'Peace and Love' hippy movement was coined by Allen Ginsberg in 1965?

4 In literature, which author wrote the James Bond spy thrillers?

5 Which *B* is a city in North Wales that has an ancient cathedral holding the tombs of Welsh princes?

6 In maths, how long would it take to travel 18 miles at six miles per hour?

7 In food, what *T* is a traditional Indian clay oven?

8 In geography, which country on the Baltic Sea lies between Sweden and Russia?

9 In the USA, is it the northern or southern states that are known as the 'Dixie States'?

10 In football, Alf Ramsey managed which country at international level?

11 In art, by what first name was the French post-Impressionist painter Gauguin known?

12 In the animal kingdom, which species of kangaroo is the largest living marsupial: red or grey?

13 What *V* is the name of a group of Caribbean islands belonging to the British Commonwealth?

14 Which American singer and songwriter was born Barry Pinkus in New York in 1946?

15 In history, which King Edward was Queen Victoria's eldest son?

16 Is the character of Agamemnon from Greek or Roman mythology?

17 In geography, on which continent would you find the Andes mountain range?

18 In film, Oliver Reed's final role was in which Hollywood blockbuster?

19 In modern history, against whom did Michael Dukakis campaign unsuccessfully in the 1988 American presidential race?

20 In 1906, the international distress signal was created, consisting of which three letters?

Previous Total

1,000

800

600

450

300

200

100

50

20

Banked

Total

Answers

1 Buddhism	**12** Red
2 Devon	**13** Virgin (Islands)
3 Flower Power	**14** Barry Manilow
4 Ian Fleming	**15** Edward VII
5 Bangor	**16** Greek
6 Three hours	**17** South America
7 Tandoor (accept	**18** *Gladiator*
tandoori)	**19** George Bush
8 Finland	(George Herbert
9 Southern	Walker Bush)
10 England	**20** SOS
11 Paul	

Round 57

1 What M is the most abundant tissue in the human body?

2 Born Vera Jayne Palmer, which blonde American film actress starred in the 1956 film *The Girl Cant Help It*?

3 In film, with which robot character is English actor Anthony Daniels most commonly associated?

4 Dead Horse Point State Park is in which American state? Utah or Arizona?

5 Which country does Arsenal's midfield player Patrick Viera represent at football?

6 In music, which US boy band had a UK number one hit in 1990 with 'Hangin' Tough'?

7 In the animal kingdom, Seal Point, Chocolate Point and Lilac Point are different breeds of which species of cat?

8 Which child's form of transport, recently popular with adults, was invented by fifteen-year-old London schoolboy Walter Lines in 1897?

9 In which year of the 1990s did the German tennis player Steffi Graf retire?

10 Did sixteenth-century British mathematician Robert Recorde invent the equals sign or the plus sign?

11 In music, which double-reeded woodwind instrument used to be known as a hautboy?

12 Which element has the chemical symbol Na?

13 In football, for which Premiership team did Roy Keane play at the beginning of 2001?

14 Is an endoskeleton internal or external?

15 What was the 1926 stoppage in which the railway, dock and power workers were called out by the Trades Union Congress called?

16 Complete the title of this Margaret Atwood novel, *The Edible . . .* what?

17 Which island is closer to the city of Miami: Cuba or Jamaica?

18 In which century did the naturalist Charles Darwin live?

19 Which D. H. Lawrence novel was banned because it was considered to be obscene: *The Rainbow* or *Women in Love*?

20 If a packet of crisps that cost 5p ten years ago now costs 50p, how many times more expensive is it?

Previous Total

1,000

800

600

450

300

200

100

50

20

Banked

Total

Answers

1 Muscle
2 Jayne Mansfield
3 C-3PO
4 Utah
5 France
6 New Kids on the Block
7 Siamese (cat)
8 Scooter
9 1999
10 Equals sign (=)
11 Oboe
12 Sodium
13 Manchester United (accept Man United/Man U)
14 Internal
15 General Strike
16 *Woman*
17 Cuba
18 Nineteenth (century)
19 *The Rainbow*
20 Ten

Round 58

1 Kerosene is turned into fuel for which type of transport?

2 With which profession would you associate Gloria Swanson?

3 Which county's tourist attractions include Woburn Abbey and Whipsnade Zoo?

4 Which boy band featured Lee, Jimmy and Spike and is also the emergency phone number in the US?

5 From which English port did the *Titanic* set sail on her maiden voyage?

6 In religion, in which century was Cardinal Basil Hume the Archbishop of Westminster?

7 The Atlantic Star and the Burma Star are types of what World War II collectibles?

8 Which member of the Osmond family became Michael Jackson's business advisor in 1987?

9 Which Scottish town was granted city status in December 2000?

10 Did the Glorious Revolution, overthrowing King James II, take place in the seventeenth or eighteenth century?

11 Rosie Boycott resigned as editor of which English newspaper in January 2001?

12 The formal name for soccer is '. . . (what) football'?

13 What *A* is the generic term for a liquid that can be added to a water-cooling system to prevent it from freezing in cold weather?

14 In which African country might you visit Amboseli, Samburu and Tsavo National Parks?

15 Alexandra Ripley's book *Scarlett* is a sequel to which novel?

16 Which *Last of the Summer Wine* star provides the voice for the animated creation Wallace in the *Wallace & Gromit* films?

17 Which war took place in South-east Asia between 1950 and 1953?

18 In which former British colony was fashion designer John Rocha born?

19 In Judaism, the Twelve Tribes of Israel were descendants of the sons of whom?

20 Who is General Secretary of the Transport and General Workers' Union?

Previous Total

1,000
800
600
450
300
200
100
50
20

Banked

Total

Answers

1 Aeroplanes (accept jet aircraft)
2 Acting
3 Bedfordshire
4 911
5 Southampton
6 Twentieth (century)
7 Medals (accept decorations)
8 (Little) Jimmy Osmond
9 Inverness
10 Seventeenth
11 *Daily Express* (accept *Express*)
12 Association (football)
13 Antifreeze
14 Kenya
15 *Gone with the Wind*
16 Peter Sallis
17 The Korean War
18 Hong Kong
19 Jacob (accept Israel)
20 Bill Morris (accept William Morris)

Round 59

1 In cockney rhyming slang, to which part of the body does your 'Barnet Fair' refer?

2 What type of drink would you be expecting if you ordered a 'G and T' from the bartender?

3 In the animal kingdom, cocker, springer and King Charles are all breeds of which dog?

4 In the human body, what A is the joint that connects the foot and the leg?

5 In nature, is a mandrake a type of plant or bird?

6 Which cartoon character's catchphrase is 'I tawt I taw a puddy tat'?

7 In fashion, slacks are a kind of what T?

8 In music, for which rock singer was the single 'I'd Do Anything For Love (But I Wont Do That)' a UK and US number one hit in 1993?

9 In science, melting is the process by which a solid becomes a what?

10 What G is a slang term referring to someone who obsessively follows a musical group or star wherever they go?

11 What does a bibliophile collect?

12 In fashion, which French designer and trendsetter created the little black dress?

13 According to tradition, what are you known as if you were born within the sound of Bow bells in Cheapside?

14 In the animal kingdom, can a tortoise crawl out of its shell?

15 In *EastEnders*, which item of Pat Evans's jewellery did Roy call vulgar?

16 Name the *Beano* comic character, Minnie the . . . what?

17 On a standard dartboard, how many points would you score if you hit double top?

18 According to the proverb, it's 'Least said, soonest . . .' what?

19 In literature, 'The Knight's Tale' and 'The Nun's Priest's Tale' are both from which collection of stories by Geoffrey Chaucer?

20 At which sport do Colin Montgomerie and John Daley compete?

Previous Total

◯

1,000

800

600

450

300

200

100

50

20

Banked

◯

◯

◯

◯

◯

Total

◯

Answers

1 Hair
2 Gin and tonic
3 Spaniel
4 Ankle (accept ankle joint)
5 Plant
6 Tweety Pie (accept Tweetie)
7 Trousers
8 Meat Loaf (Marvin Lee Aday)
9 Liquid
10 Groupie
11 Books
12 (Coco) Chanel (Gabrielle Bonheur Chanel)
13 Cockney
14 No
15 Earrings
16 Minx
17 40
18 Mended
19 *The Canterbury Tales*
20 Golf

Round 60

1 Which ex-*EastEnders* actor presented the children's TV show *Runaround*?

2 Which gravel-voiced rock star had a 1978 number one hit in the UK and America with 'Do Ya Think I'm Sexy'?

3 Which famous fashion designer has the initials YSL?

4 If you bought seven lollipops at 12p each, how much would you spend?

5 In British nobility, what is the correct form of address for a duke: 'Your Grace' or 'My Lord'?

6 According to superstition, what is considered lucky if hung the right way up or unlucky if hung upside-down?

7 In the animal kingdom, which is larger, the male or female emu?

8 In food, the pasta *conchiglie* is shaped like what?

9 In language, what *H* is the name commonly used to describe the after-effects of being badly drunk?

10 In music, 'World In Motion' was a number one hit in 1990 for which country's World Cup squad?

11 In nature, what is the name of the imaginary line that encircles the middle of the Earth halfway between the North and South Poles?

12 In language, what *M* describes a society in which the mother is the head of the family?

13 Which *EastEnders* character left the soap in the year 2000 by driving off into the sunset to Spain?

14 Which Shakespeare play features the line 'Is this a dagger which I see before me?'?

15 In the animal kingdom, are crocodiles warm-blooded or cold-blooded animals?

16 In geography, which is the longest river in South America?

17 In theatre, an audience's summons for actors to take a bow after the performance is known as a 'curtain . . .' what?

18 What was the character name of Mrs Merton's son in her TV sitcom and chat show?

19 In cockney rhyming slang, which parts of the body are your 'bacon and eggs'?

20 The famous public school The King's College of Our Lady, near Windsor, is better known by what other name?

Previous Total

◯

1,000

800

600

450

300

200

100

50

20

Banked

◯

◯

◯

◯

◯

Total

◯

Answers

1 Mike Reid
2 Rod Stewart
3 Yves Saint-Laurent
4 84p
5 Your Grace
6 Horseshoe
7 Female
8 Shells (accept snails)
9 Hangover
10 England
11 Equator
12 Matriarchy
13 Irene Raymond (accept Irene)
14 *Macbeth*
15 Cold-blooded
16 Amazon
17 (Curtain) call
18 Malcolm
19 Legs
20 Eton (Eton College)

Round 61

1 In medicine, what name is given to people who suffer from an exaggerated concern about their health?

2 The guitarist Brian May is married to which former *EastEnders* actress?

3 If you were born on the fourth of July, what would be your zodiacal star sign?

4 In American sport, The Super . . . *what* is the final of the National Football League?

5 In 1671, Thomas Blood broke into the Tower of London with three accomplices. What did they try to steal?

6 In pop music, what was Lionel Richie dancing on, in the title of his 1986 hit?

7 With which sport is Virginia Wade associated?

8 In pop music, complete the title of this 1999 single by Engelbert Humperdinck: 'Quando Quando . . .' what?

9 Denzel Washington starred as which controversial Black nationalist leader in the 1992 film of the same name?

10 In maths, add the number of hours in a day to the number of minutes in an hour.

11 In *EastEnders*, which character cajoled Phil into starting the car-lot fire?

12 A bottle labelled with a picture of a flame contains a substance with which particular hazardous property?

13 What word can both describe a male goose and is a slang term meaning 'to look'?

14 Which boy band featured in U2's video for 'Sweetest Thing', Boyzone or Take That?

15 In children's television, Zammo, Tucker and Pogo were characters from which London comprehensive?

16 In food, which *T* is a pink-coloured Greek appetiser made from fish roe?

17 In modern history, what *R* is the Hindi name given to the British rule in India?

18 Martin and Gary Kemp from the pop group Spandau Ballet starred together in which 1990 film?

19 Which Scottish city was designated the European City of Culture in 1990?

20 What *O* is the name given to minerals from which substances such as metals can be extracted?

Previous Total
1,000
800
600
450
300
200
100
50
20
Banked
Total

Answers

1 Hypochondriac (accept valetudinarian/ phrenesiac)
2 Anita Dobson
3 Cancer
4 (Super) Bowl
5 Crown jewels
6 The Ceiling
7 Tennis
8 'Quando'
9 Malcolm X
10 84
11 Frank Butcher
12 Flammability (accept inflammability/it will catch fire)
13 Gander
14 Boyzone
15 Grange Hill
16 Taramasalata
17 Raj
18 *The Krays*
19 Glasgow
20 Ore(s)

Round 62

1 Which Birmingham-born actress appeared as the character Mrs Wilkinson in the 2000 film *Billy Elliot*?

2 What name is given to an American ten-cent piece?

3 Which famous board game was advertised with the quote 'Every American is entitled to Life, Liberty and the Pursuit of Trivia'?

4 In Australia, is a 'kylie' a type of outdoor party or a boomerang?

5 In geography, what is the name of the two sets of imaginary lines used to locate position on the globe?

6 In England, the day before Lent is traditionally called 'Shrove . . .' what?

7 What was the name of the Chinese dynasty that reigned from 1368 to 1644?

8 Which of the two Houses of Parliament contains a shooting range?

9 In *EastEnders*, which business in the Square is owned by the ever-absent Mr Papadopoulos?

10 Iberian Airways is the national airline of which country?

11 In sport, what is the name of the field game in which points are scored by throwing a small ball into a goal with a netted stick?

12 Which famous Italian dictator was born the son of a socialist blacksmith in 1883?

13 A laryngoscope is an instrument for examining which area of the body?

14 In the New Testament, Death rides which animal: a pale horse or a dark horse?

15 In the TV sitcom *Friends*, what is Joey's occupation?

16 In French, 'poussin' is a word used to describe what type of baby creature?

17 Which of the following characters did *not* appear in the first episode of *EastEnders*: Nick Cotton, Angie Watts or Dot Cotton?

18 In nature, what K is a common brown seaweed?

19 In which English county are the towns of Bodmin and Truro?

20 The raven is a member of which bird family?

Previous Total

1,000

800

600

450

300

200

100

50

20

Banked

Total

Answers

1 Julie Walters
2 Dime
3 Trivial Pursuit
4 Boomerang
5 Latitude and longitude
6 Tuesday
7 Ming dynasty
8 House of Lords
9 The launderette
10 Spain
11 Lacrosse
12 Benito Mussolini (accept Mussolini)
13 Larynx (accept throat)
14 A pale horse
15 Actor
16 Chicken (accept hen/chick)
17 Dot Cotton
18 Kelp
19 Cornwall
20 Crow (accept Corvidae)

Round 63

1 Which superhero cartoon bear of the 1980s had a sidekick called Spotty?

2 Which actor played the character Jack Colton in the films *Romancing the Stone* and *The Jewel of the Nile*?

3 Which former England football manager joined Middlesbrough in the year 2000?

4 In nature, what *D* is the common name applied to the large, extinct flightless birds native to Mauritius?

5 In which European country is Bremen?

6 In the TV soap *EastEnders*, what was the name of Pauline Fowler's twin brother?

7 In cricket, Sir Richard Hadlee became the first test player to take the field with which honour in 1990?

8 Apache and Navaho are both tribes of which indigenous people?

9 In which European country was Leonardo da Vinci born?

10 In history, William Bligh was commander of which ship when his crew mutinied in 1789?

11 In Charles Dickens's novel *The Pickwick Papers*, is Nathaniel Pipkin a parish clerk or parish priest?

12 In which year 2000 film directed by Guy Ritchie did Brad Pitt star as One Punch Mickey O'Neil?

13 In fashion, what riding breeches take their name from a former state in north-west India?

14 In *EastEnders*, how many times has Mark Fowler been married?

15 In geography, on which Greek island is the ancient city of Knossos found?

16 Anthracite contains over 90 per cent carbon and is the purest form of what fuel?

17 In the TV series *The Dukes of Hazzard*, was Luke Duke Bo Duke's cousin or brother?

18 In theatre, which British composer of musicals has the official title Baron of Sydmonton?

19 Did Barry Micklethwaite go into the *Guinness Book of Records* in November 2000 for growing the world's largest carrot or parsnip?

20 Which bay in Cuba was invaded by exiles opposed to Fidel Castro in 1961?

Answers

1 Superted
2 Michael Douglas (Michael Kirk Douglas)
3 Terry Venables
4 Dodo (accept *Raphus cucullatus*)
5 Germany
6 Peter Beale (accept Pete/Peter)
7 Knighthood
8 Native Americans (accept American Indians/North American Indians/ Red Indians)
9 Italy
10 The *Bounty*
11 Parish clerk
12 *Snatch*
13 Jodhpurs
14 Twice (accept two)
15 Crete
16 Coal
17 Cousin
18 (Sir) Andrew Lloyd Webber (accept Lord Lloyd Webber)
19 Parsnip
20 The Bay of Pigs (accept Bahia de los Cochinos)

Previous Total

1,000
800
600
450
300
200
100
50
20

Banked

Total

Round 64

1 Which *EastEnders* actress played the character Nannie Slagg in the TV drama series *Gormenghast*?

2 In British politics, the acronym SERPS refers to a state scheme relating to what?

3 Which hilly area in north central England was designated the UK's first National Park in 1951?

4 Which actor appeared as English teacher John Keating in the 1989 film *Dead Poets' Society*?

5 Which acoustic musical instrument usually has a damper pedal, often known as a loud pedal?

6 Which herb shares its name with a character in the comedy series *Fawlty Towers*?

7 Does the flag of Texas have one or ten stars on it?

8 Which US heavyweight boxer suffered his first ever defeat as a professional against James Buster Douglas in 1990?

9 Which 1973 horror film about a young girl possessed by a demon was based on a book by William Peter Blatty?

10 In *EastEnders*, which character did Hattie Tavernier knee in the groin after he tried to kiss her?

11 Peeping Tom and King Alfred are varieties of which spring flower?

12 Is Paris's Rive Gauche the left or right bank of the Seine?

13 What F is the name given to frozen dew or fog?

14 Which ship, used by Nelson in the Battle of Trafalgar, is a Portsmouth tourist attraction?

15 Which river is longer, the Nile or the Ganges?

16 In Greek mythology, which hero battled with the legendary nine-headed monster Hydra?

17 In maths, if you buy four stamps at 18p each, how much have you spent?

18 In geography, the city of Port Elizabeth is in which African country?

19 Which star played Jack Carter in the 2000 remake of *Get Carter*?

20 What was Beethoven's first name?

Previous Total

1,000
800
600
450
300
200
100
50
20

Banked

Total

Answers

1 June Brown (do not accept Dot Cotton)
2 Pensions (accept pension schemes/ pension provision)
3 Peak District
4 Robin Williams (Robin McLaurim Williams)
5 Piano (accept pianola/pianoforte)
6 Basil
7 One
8 Mike Tyson
9 *The Exorcist*
10 Ian Beale
11 Daffodil (accept narcissus/trumpet narcissus/common daffodil)
12 Left (bank)
13 Frost
14 HMS *Victory* (accept *Victory*)
15 Nile
16 Hercules (accept Heracles)
17 72p
18 South Africa
19 Sylvester Stallone (Sylvester Enzio Stallone)
20 Ludwig

Round 65

1 Which famous pop artist once said 'In the future, everyone will be famous for fifteen minutes'?

2 According to the nursery rhyme, whose cupboard was so bare that she couldn't feed her dog?

3 In astronomy, which *P* is the ninth planet from the sun?

4 What *S* is a woolly farm animal, the male of which is called a ram?

5 In pop music, complete the title of this Madonna song: 'Crazy For . . .' who?

6 What *C* is the British name given to a wafer-thin slice of potato that has been fried and is eaten cold as a snack?

7 Of whom is St Christopher the patron saint?

8 In nature, which small, yellow-and-white flower is traditionally joined together to make a chain?

9 Were dinosaurs reptiles or mammals?

10 In music, which Scottish singer had her first UK hit in 1964 with a cover of the song 'Shout'?

11 Eeyore the donkey featured in which children's books?

12 What colour does William Wallace paint his face in the 1995 film *Braveheart*?

13 What *G* is the collective term for the parts of a chicken removed before cooking and often used for stock?

14 In an orchestra, which family of musical instruments are normally played with a bow?

15 According to the proverb, 'a trouble shared is a trouble . . .' what?

16 In science, what rumbling sound is caused by air expanding rapidly as it is heated by flashes of lightning?

17 In the TV series *The Muppet Show*, what sort of animal was the piano-playing Rowlf?

18 In medieval legend, what name was given to the dish or cup used by Jesus at the Last Supper?

19 In maths, add the number of sides on an octagon to the number of months of the year.

20 In human biology, eczema is a condition that affects which part of the body?

Previous Total

1,000

800

600

450

300

200

100

50

20

Banked

Total

Answers

1 Andy Warhol (Andrew Warhola)	**12** Blue (accept blue and white)
2 Old Mother Hubbard	**13** Giblets
3 Pluto	**14** Violin family (accept strings/stringed instruments)
4 Sheep	
5 You	
6 Crisp	**15** Halved
7 Travellers (accept motorists)	**16** Thunder
	17 Dog
8 Daisy	**18** The Holy Grail (accept Grail)
9 Reptiles	
10 Lulu (accept Lulu and the Luvvers)	**19** 20
	20 Skin
11 Winnie the Pooh	

Round 66

1 In the animal kingdom, 'spotted camel' was the name given by the Romans to which very tall African mammal?

2 In Greek mythology, the Gorgon's hair consisted of what type of creatures?

3 What *W* is the popular name for the gas capsule intended to make canned beer taste like draught?

4 Complete the title of the 1993 film starring Mel Gibson: *The Man Without a . . .* what?

5 In athletics, Roger Black was known for running which distance: 100, 400 or 800 metres?

6 In human biology, what *N* is the name given to the flattened, horny coverings on the upper surface of the fingers and toes?

7 In children's television, Sandy and Bud were characters in which Florida Keys-based drama about a dolphin?

8 Who played Neo in the 1999 film *The Matrix*?

9 If there is a 20 per cent discount on a dress that was £100, what is the discounted price?

10 In nature, what *S* is a mollusc commonly found in the garden that has a protective shell covering its body?

11 Who duetted with Janet Jackson on the 1992 hit 'The Best Things In Life Are Free': Luther Vandross or Lionel Richie?

12 Which Hindu god is both the Destroyer and the Restorer?

13 In humans, what *T* is the part of the body associated with the word 'guttural'?

14 According to the Bible, was Jonah in the belly of the great fish for three or eleven days?

15 If a floor's dimensions are 8 metres by 9 metres, what is the floor's area in square metres?

16 What is produced by a spider's spinnerets?

17 In the children's TV programme, who only came out to play when Andy Pandy and Teddy weren't looking?

18 Is hypertension a condition of high or low blood pressure?

19 Coke, gas, tar and oil are all by-products of the processing of which fossil fuel?

20 Who is the Oscar-winning daughter of Judy Garland and Vincente Minnelli?

Previous Total

1,000
800
600
450
300
200
100
50
20

Banked

Total

Answers

1 Giraffe
2 Snakes (accept serpents)
3 Widget
4 Face
5 400 metres
6 Nail(s)
7 Flipper
8 Keanu Reeves (K. C. Reeves/Chuck Spidena)
9 £80
10 Snail
11 Luther Vandross
12 Shiva
13 Throat (accept thyroid artery)
14 Three
15 72 (square metres)
16 Silk (accept web/gossamer/thread)
17 Looby Loo
18 High
19 Coal
20 Liza Minnelli (Liza May Minnelli)

Round 67

1 In the animal kingdom, what C is a ground squirrel, native to North American and Asian forests, with a black-and-white striped back?

2 In which sport would you find the positions 'silly mid on' and 'short leg'?

3 Which star sign would you have if you were born on 13 September?

4 Which American actor interviews a vampire in a 1994 film starring Tom Cruise and Brad Pitt?

5 In geography, what A is a tourist resort and port near Benidorm in south-eastern Spain?

6 In the animal kingdom, what O is an aquatic mammal which lives in a holt?

7 In classical music, what type of voice is a countertenor: male or female?

8 In the UK, when wiring a plug, what colour is the neutral wire?

9 In football, which club temporarily shared Maine Road with Manchester City between 1941 and 1949 because of bomb damage to their own ground?

10 Which Irish DJ and TV presenter's autobiography is entitled *Is It Me?*?

11 Which country is further south, Singapore or Sri Lanka?

12 What is the name given to a male hare or rabbit?

13 How is the umbilicus more commonly known?

14 In nature, what *M* is a type of grass with very small seeds, often fed to budgies?

15 Is Tchaikovsky's *The Sleeping Beauty* an opera or a ballet?

16 In law, what *E* is the crime of fraudulently retaining money or goods entrusted to you?

17 Which country lies along the western coast of Scandinavia?

18 Which animal did north-eastern fishermen nickname a 'grunter' because they believed saying its name would bring bad luck?

19 A sudden torrent of water caused by heavy rain is known as a '. . . (*what*) flood'?

20 Michelangelo and which other Italian artist were commissioned to paint battle scenes on the walls of the city hall in Florence?

Previous Total

1,000

800

600

450

300

200

100

50

20

Banked

Total

Answers

1 Chipmunk	**10** Terry Wogan
2 Cricket	**11** Singapore
3 Virgo	**12** Buck
4 Christian Slater (Christian Michael Leonard Hawkins)	**13** Navel (accept belly button/tummy button)
5 Alicante	**14** Millet
6 Otter	**15** Ballet
7 Male	**16** Embezzlement
8 Blue	**17** Norway
9 Manchester United (accept Man United/Man U)	**18** Pig
	19 Flash (flood)
	20 Leonardo da Vinci (accept Leonardo)

Round 68

1 Mount Godwin-Austin in the Karakoram Range is more commonly known by which letter and number?

2 Which pop star caused a stir in 2000 when he appeared to peel off his skin in his video *Rock DJ*?

3 In nature, what is a bird able to do when it has fledged?

4 In horse racing, what *D* is a famous flat race for three-year-olds run over one-and-a-half miles at Epsom in early June?

5 Is the highway that runs north from Brisbane called the Bruce Highway or the Sheila Highway?

6 In literature, Jim Hawkins is the narrator of which Robert Louis Stevenson novel?

7 In politics, which environmental pressure group has the initials FoE?

8 In maths, how long would it take to travel 110 miles at 55 miles per hour?

9 In biology, Italian anatomist Gabriel Fallopius gave his name to which part of a female mammal's internal organs?

10 What is the longest river in France?

11 In art, rounds, mops and flats are all types of which tool?

12 Which city in Switzerland was designated as the European centre for the United Nations in 1947?

13 What is the name of Kirk Douglas's actor–producer son, who starred in the film *Fatal Attraction*?

14 In geography, which has the greater area, France or the state of Texas?

15 In the animal kingdom, after a koala is born, where on its mother's body is it carried?

16 In history, what was the nickname of Tsar Peter I of Russia?

17 In religion, what K is the name of the Hindu and Buddhist idea that past actions determine a person's fate?

18 In pop, which of the Beatles said 'The Beatles can't save the world. We'll be lucky if we can save ourselves'?

19 What type of sport is played annually at the Orange Bowl in Miami?

20 In British banking, what is the lowest rate of interest payable on loans, which acts as the benchmark for other interest rates, called?

Previous Total

1,000
800
600
450
300
200
100
50
20

Banked

Total

Answers

1 K2
2 Robbie Williams (Robert Peter Maximillian Williams)
3 Fly
4 Derby
5 Bruce Highway
6 *Treasure Island*
7 Friends of the Earth
8 2 hours
9 Fallopian tubes
10 The Loire
11 Brush(es)
12 Geneva
13 Michael Douglas
14 Texas
15 Pouch
16 Peter the Great
17 Karma
18 George Harrison
19 American football
20 Base rate (accept repo rate)

Round 69

1 Who invented the clockwork radio in 1993?

2 Did the 1919 Sex Disqualification Removal Act enable women to work in all professions or to vote?

3 In comics, Walter the Softy was regularly tormented by which naughty child?

4 Who wrote the play *The Cocktail Party* in 1949?

5 What honour did actor Alec Guinness receive from the Queen in 1959?

6 Which 1982 science-fiction film starring Harrison Ford had the tag line 'Man Has Made His Match – Now It's His Problem'?

7 In human biology, the villi are found projecting from the walls of the small . . . what?

8 In literature, in which E. M. Forster novel, written in 1924, does the character Doctor Aziz appear?

9 What is the capital city of Malaysia?

10 In football, Gianfranco Zola played for which country at international level?

11 In geography, near which coastal resort in south Devon would you find Kent's Cavern?

12 What term is used when a beam of light spreads: deflection or diffraction?

13 In politics, to what British party did Sir Anthony Eden belong?

14 In the Harry Potter books, the Hogwarts Express leaves from which London train station?

15 Complete the title of the martial arts film, *Crouching Tiger, Hidden . . .* what?

16 In language, what is the English translation for the Spanish word '*mañana*'?

17 In Christianity, in which month of the year is Epiphany celebrated?

18 What was the name given to the night-time German air raids during the Second World War?

19 Which British actress was born Brenda Bottle in 1946 and nominated for a Golden Globe award for her performance in the film *Saving Grace*?

20 In children's literature, who wrote the Paddington Bear books?

Previous Total
1,000
800
600
450
300
200
100
50
20
Banked
Total

Answers

1 Trevor Bayliss	**11** Torquay
2 Work in all professions	**12** Diffraction
	13 Conservative
3 Dennis the Menace	**14** King's Cross
4 T. S. Eliot	**15** *Dragon*
5 Knighthood	**16** Morning or tomorrow
6 *Blade Runner*	**17** January
7 Intestine	**18** The Blitz
8 *A Passage to India*	**19** Brenda Blethyn
9 Kuala Lumpur	**20** Michael Bond
10 Italy	

1 Was Prometheus a figure in Greek or Roman mythology?

2 In science, what *D* is the mass of a substance per unit of volume?

3 In the *Rocky* series of films, starring Sylvester Stallone, what was Rocky's surname?

4 In science, how many states of matter are there?

5 What is the name of the US evangelist who has been touring the world on his crusades since 1950?

6 Complete the title of this John Irving novel: *A Prayer for . . .* who?

7 In television, which *Dad's Army* character observed that 'They don't like it up 'em'?

8 If a candle has a 50-hour burn time, how many hours has it left to burn if only one-fifth of the candle remains?

9 In history, what was the East India Company founded in 1600 to trade in?

10 In music, in which country was the Philadelphia Orchestra founded in 1900?

11 In geography, Panama lies between Costa Rica and which other country?

12 In UK politics, what was John Major's position in the Conservative government before becoming party leader?

13 In geography, the Republic of Ireland is divided into how many provinces?

14 In science, is iron an element or an alloy?

15 Which actor has starred in the films *Donnie Brasco, Edward Scissorhands* and *Sleepy Hollow*?

16 In pastimes, what do tegestologists collect from pubs?

17 In which decade was the Rugby Super League set up?

18 Which Lancashire fishing port stands at the mouth of the River Wyre?

19 Which sport would you play at Flushing Meadows Center in New York?

20 In pop music, whose 1986 album was entitled *Graceland*?

Previous Total
1,000
800
600
450
300
200
100
50
20
Banked
Total

Answers

1 Greek
2 Density
3 Balboa
4 Three
5 Billy Graham (William Franklin Graham)
6 Owen Meany
7 Lance Corporal Jack Jones (accept Corporal Jones/ Jonesy)
8 10 hours
9 Spices
10 United States (accept US/USA/United States of America/America)

11 Colombia
12 Chancellor of the Exchequer
13 Four
14 Element
15 Johnny Depp
16 Beer mats
17 1990s (accept nineties) (1996)
18 Fleetwood
19 Tennis
20 Paul Simon

Round 71

1 Where was the original Disneyland: Florida or California?

2 In human biology, what organ is affected by bronchitis?

3 In history, the mutiny on the HMS *Bounty* happened in which century?

4 In what sport do you require a map and a compass to negotiate a specified course on foot?

5 In geography, what is the collective name given to the counties in close proximity to London?

6 In religion, which fruit is described in the Koran as the fruit of a tree in paradise: peach, banana or apple?

7 What K is the name of the police force featured in Mack Sennett's silent film comedies?

8 In science, do waves of gamma radiation travel faster than light waves?

9 In marine biology, is a ray's mouth generally on the upper or lower side of its body?

10 In food, from which country does mozzarella originate?

11 In nature, from which tree would you pick conkers?

12 In pop music, complete the title of this Monkees song: 'Last Train to . . .' what?

13 In fifteenth-century literature, Sir Thomas Malory is credited with the first prose account of the legend of which king?

14 In Giza, Egypt, what famous monument has the body of a lion and the head of a man?

15 What was the nationality of the exotic dancer Mata Hari who was executed in 1917 as a spy?

16 In nature, an aerobic creature relies on what gas in the atmosphere?

17 In television, which G was a children's drama series beginning in 1978, documenting life in a comprehensive school?

18 In the animal kingdom, what V is a type of venomous snake with long, folding fangs?

19 In politics, what is the US equivalent of the British cabinet post of foreign secretary?

20 Is the Gobi desert situated in the northern or the southern hemisphere?

Previous Total

( )

1,000

800

600

450

300

200

100

50

20

Banked

( )

( )

( )

( )

( )

Total

( )

Answers

1 California
2 Lungs
3 Eighteenth century (1789)
4 Orienteering
5 Home counties
6 Banana
7 Keystone Cops
8 No (they travel at the same speed)
9 Lower (side)
10 Italy
11 Horse chestnut
12 Clarksville
13 (King) Arthur
14 The Great Sphinx (accept sphinx)
15 Dutch
16 Oxygen
17 Grange Hill
18 Viper
19 Secretary of State
20 Northern

Round 72

1 In human biology, which S is the part of the body affected by eczema?

2 In what year did the giant letters 'Hollywood' go up on a hill above Los Angeles: 1923 or 1933?

3 Which Calvin is an American fashion designer famous for his line in men's underwear?

4 Which American inventor was known as the Wizard of Menlo Park: Thomas Edison or Wilbur Wright?

5 In politics, what N is the word that is used when a business or industry is taken into public ownership?

6 Complete the title of the following Lewis Carroll classic poem: 'The Hunting of . . .'.

7 In rugby, who has scored most international tries for England, Jeremy Guscott or Rory Underwood?

8 Which classical instrument is Julian Lloyd Webber famous for playing?

9 In nature, on oak trees, do the male or female flowers ripen into acorns?

10 In human biology, what T is another name for the chest?

11 In British television, during what decade were The Adventures of Rin Tin Tin first broadcast?

12 What E is a reference book summarising all human knowledge?

13 A fox chases a hen for 20 metres. How long is this in centimetres?

14 In food, what type of salad leaf shares its name with a vehicle designed for space travel?

15 On an Ordnance Survey map, for what does 'P' stand?

16 In nature, do European ladybirds hibernate in the winter?

17 Which famous photographer married supermodel Marie Helvin in 1975?

18 In which century was the US pioneer and adventurer Davy Crockett born, the seventeenth or eighteenth?

19 In sport, in what English city can you find the Rugby Union team the Tigers and the football team the Foxes?

20 What is the name of the largest lake in Africa?

Previous Total

1,000

800

600

450

300

200

100

50

20

Banked

Total

Answers

1 Skin	**11** 1950s
2 1923	**12** Encyclopaedia
3 Calvin Klein	**13** 2,000 centimetres
4 Thomas Edison	**14** Rocket
5 Nationalisation	**15** Post Office
6 The Snark	**16** Yes
7 Rory Underwood	**17** David Bailey
8 Cello (accept	**18** Eighteenth century
violoncello)	(1786–1836)
9 Female	**19** Leicester
10 Thorax	**20** Victoria

Round 73

1 In geography, is the county of Tipperary in Northern Ireland or the Republic of Ireland?

2 In religion, which chemical element was known as brimstone: sulphur, carbon or aluminium?

3 In classical music, what was the composer Wolfgang Mozart's middle name?

4 To which country did Shirley Valentine go on holiday in the 1989 film starring Pauline Collins?

5 A molecule of water is made up of two atoms of hydrogen and one atom of what?

6 In the USA, Dulles International Airport is just outside which city: Seattle or Washington, DC?

7 Complete the name of this 1960s pop band: Dave Dee, Dozy, Beaky, Mic and what?

8 What type of insect is a firefly: a fly or a beetle?

9 What A is a book consisting of a series of literary selections?

10 What item of cutlery did Uri Geller become famous for bending in the early 1970s?

11 What nationality is fashion designer Issey Miyake?

12 On some types of fishing hook, what B is the name of the sharp point which faces away from the main tip?

13 In the Grimm's fairy tale, who left a trail of breadcrumbs to find their way home?

14 Is Los Angeles behind or ahead of Greenwich Mean Time?

15 In ancient history, what *P* was the name given to the common, poor people of ancient Rome?

16 In the animal kingdom, do tortoises lay eggs or give birth to live young?

17 In a camera, what *A* is the name given to the opening that allows light to pass through the lens onto the film?

18 In film, in which year was the first *Star Wars* movie released: 1975, 1977 or 1979?

19 Whom does the organisation UNICEF assist or protect?

20 In which sport played on a lawn is there a stroke called a 'roquet'?

Previous Total

1,000

800

600

450

300

200

100

50

20

Banked

Total

Answers

1 Republic of Ireland	**12** Barb
2 Sulphur	**13** Hansel and Gretel
3 Amadeus	**14** Behind
4 Greece	**15** Plebeians (accept
5 Oxygen	plebs)
6 Washington, DC	**16** Lay eggs
7 Tich	**17** Aperture
8 Beetle	**18** 1977
9 Anthology	**19** Children
10 Spoons	**20** Croquet
11 Japanese	

Round 74

1 Which *B* is a card game in which you play a rubber?

2 In the percussion section of an orchestra, what *T* are large, tuned drums, sometimes known as kettle drums?

3 In religion, St Swithin is buried in which cathedral: St Paul's, Winchester or Coventry?

4 In transport, what *A* is a device operated by the foot that controls the speed of a vehicle?

5 Name the long-running BBC TV series which centred on a character called James Herriot.

6 A candle is 9 centimetres high. As it burns, it shrinks 32 millimetres. How tall is it now, in millimetres?

7 In history, in which century did the Reformation occur: the sixteenth or seventeenth?

8 Created by T. S. Eliot, what kind of animal are Mr Mistoffelees, Macavity and Gus?

9 In literature, which doctor was taught by his parrot, Polynesia, to understand the language of animals?

10 Which major river firth would you have to cross in going from St Andrews to Dundee by the most direct route?

11 In which English county would you find the city of St Albans and the town of Watford?

12 By what name is the molten rock discharged in a stream by a volcano known?

13 In what decade was the Family Allowance Act introduced to give payments to parents: the 1920s, 1930s or 1940s?

14 What Holly is the American actress who starred in *Broadcast News* and *The Piano*?

15 Las Palmas is a city in which island group?

16 According to the poet Byron, the English winter ends in July, to recommence when, August or September?

17 What S is the Mexican dish which is salad, sauce and relish, all in one?

18 What film company did Charlie Chaplin, Douglas Fairbanks, Mary Pickford and D. W. Griffith form in 1919?

19 In which US state is Big Bend National Park located: Texas or California?

20 Which ancient city provided David Gray with a hit single?

Previous Total

1,000

800

600

450

300

200

100

50

20

Banked

Total

Answers

1 Bridge	**11** Hertfordshire
2 Timpani	**12** Lava (accept magma)
3 Winchester	**13** 1940s
4 Accelerator	**14** Hunter
5 *All Creatures Great and Small*	**15** Canary Islands
	16 August
6 58 millimetres	**17** Salsa
7 Sixteenth century	**18** United Artists
8 Cats	**19** Texas
9 Doctor Dolittle	**20** Babylon
10 (Firth of) Tay	

Round 75

1 Does the Indian Ocean lie off the east or west coast of Australia?

2 What S is produced from plants such as corn and grass, stored in a silo for use as animal fodder?

3 In the United States, the Democrats are one of the main political parties, which is the other?

4 In biology, what B is the name for the thick layer of fat under the skin of marine mammals?

5 In 1939, the BBC television service closed down for the duration of the Second World War; which cartoon character featured in the last programme transmitted?

6 On the world wide web, which country do the letters '.hk' represent?

7 What H is the name given to a tropical cyclone, also known as a typhoon?

8 Canute became king of which country in 1016?

9 Is the town of Dumbarton to be found near the Firth of Clyde or Firth of Forth?

10 How many hours behind GMT is Central Standard Time?

11 What H is a large, fish-eating, wading bird with long legs and a long pointed bill?

12 In pop music, which American state featured in the title of UK hit singles by The Beach Boys and The Mamas and the Papas?

13 What is the name of the museum of decorative arts in London's South Kensington founded in the nineteenth century?

14 Who wrote the play *Antony and Cleopatra*?

15 Do grapefruit grow on vines or trees?

16 Which Bob Fosse film musical was released in 1972 and starred Liza Minnelli?

17 In medicine, if you had to visit a dermatologist, which part of your body would be affected?

18 In art, Sir William Chambers designed a pagoda for which London botanical garden?

19 Which *D* is a sea mammal known for breathing through a blowhole on the top of its head?

20 What character did Julie Newmar and Eartha Kitt both play in the 1960s *Batman* TV series?

Previous Total

1,000

800

600

450

300

200

100

50

20

Banked

Total

Answers

1 West	**12** California
2 Silage (ensilage)	**13** Victoria & Albert
3 Republicans	Museum
4 Blubber	**14** William Shakespeare
5 Mickey Mouse	**15** Trees
6 Hong Kong	**16** *Cabaret*
7 Hurricane	**17** Skin
8 England	**18** Kew
9 Firth of Clyde	**19** Dolphin
10 6 (Six)	**20** Catwoman
11 Heron	

Round 76

1 In science, what Q is the smallest amount of energy that a system can gain or lose?

2 In television, name the army sergeant played by Phil Silvers in the US sitcom *The Phil Silvers Show*.

3 Which brother is the famous father of Anaïs Gallagher: Noel or Liam?

4 In literature, who wrote *Robinson Crusoe* in 1719?

5 On which river does the city of Leeds stand?

6 In pop music, which male artist had a hit in both 1976 and 1994 with 'Don't Go Breaking My Heart'?

7 In food, what C is a waxy substance found in animal fats, which can cause clogging of the arteries?

8 In what year was the first mass-produced personal computer launched in the UK: 1977 or 1981?

9 In *The Jungle Book*, what type of animal is Bagheera?

10 The BBC pre-school slot which featured the shows *Andy Pandy* and *Bill and Ben, the Flowerpot Men,* was called *Watch with . . .* whom?

11 'The Wild Wood' and 'The Piper at the Gates of Dawn' are chapters from which children's book by Kenneth Grahame?

12 In which year was France liberated from German occupation during the Second World War?

13 In politics, which party was in power from 1964 to 1970, Labour or Conservative?

14 By what name is the Italian city of Firenze usually known in Britain?

15 What name is given to the study of the embryo?

16 In the animal kingdom, how many species of racoon are there, eight or eighteen?

17 Which 1981 film is about the runners Eric Liddell and Harold Abrahams?

18 In nature, which bird gives its nest a smooth mud lining: a song thrush or a blackbird?

19 What is the English translation for the German phrase 'Auf Wiedersehen'?

20 In television, which 1960s singing star appeared in both Budgie and Love Hurts?

Previous Total

( )

1,000

800

600

450

300

200

100

50

20

Banked

( )

( )

( )

( )

( )

Total

( )

Answers

1 Quantum
2 Bilko (Sergeant Ernie Bilko)
3 Noel
4 Daniel Defoe
5 Air
6 Elton John
7 Cholesterol (accept cholesterin)
8 1977
9 Panther (accept black panther)
10 Mother (accept Watch With Mother)
11 The Wind in the Willows
12 1944
13 Labour
14 Florence
15 Embryology
16 18
17 Chariots of Fire
18 Song thrush
19 Goodbye (until we meet again/see you later)
20 Adam Faith (accept Terence Nelhams/ Terence Nelhams-Wright)

Round 77

1 Which Beatles member said, 'Will the people in the cheaper seats clap your hands? All the rest of you, if you'll just rattle your jewellery'?

2 Complete the title of the following 1986 Paul Simon hit single. 'You Can Call Me . . .' what?

3 In which decade was the Hubble space telescope launched?

4 Are elephants omnivores or herbivores?

5 With which sport would you associate Peter Scudamore?

6 Did the North Korean government invade South Korea, setting off the Korean War, in 1950 or 1953?

7 In the human body, what would you expect to find developing within an amniotic sac?

8 Would a snood be worn above or below the waist?

9 In football, which Premiership team was Peter Taylor managing when he took over from Kevin Keegan as England's caretaker manager in October 2000?

10 In what year was the first surgical facelift performed by Eugene Hollander: 1901 or 1921?

11 Which Ernest wrote the 1929 novel *A Farewell to Arms*?

12 What type of cuddly children's toy was inspired by US president Theodore Roosevelt's hunting trip in 1902?

13 In the animal kingdom, rabbits live in burrows underground. Do hares?

14 Which Nazi parachuted into Britain in 1941 on an unlikely peace mission, dying in Spandau prison in 1987?

15 In Greek mythology, is Pandora or Athena the goddess of wisdom and war?

16 In nature, what *H* is the art and science of growing flowers, fruit and vegetables?

17 Which 6,000-acre forest in Essex is owned by the Corporation of London?

18 Whose albums include *The Rise and Fall of Ziggy Stardust* and *The Spiders from Mars*?

19 In food, what *M* is a word given to a Swiss dish of cereal, fruit and nuts, eaten with milk?

20 In film, which British actor played the roles of Alfie Elkins and Harry Palmer?

Previous Total

1,000

800

600

450

300

200

100

50

20

Banked

Total

Answers

1 John Lennon	**11** Ernest Hemingway
2 Al	**12** Teddy bear
3 The 1990s (1990)	**13** No (above ground)
4 Herbivores	**14** Rudolf Hess (accept
5 Horse racing (accept	Walter Richard)
steeplechasing/	**15** Athena
National Hunt racing)	**16** Horticulture
6 1950	**17** Epping (Forest)
7 Embryo, foetus	**18** David Bowie (accept
(accept baby, infant)	David Robert Jones)
8 Above (it's a hood or	**19** Muesli
a hairnet)	**20** Michael Caine
9 Leicester City	(Maurice Joseph
10 1901	Micklewhite)

Round 78

1 What was the family name of the last tsar of Russia, Nicholas II, who was murdered in 1918?

2 In golf, against whom do the USA play for the Ryder Cup?

3 What word is used to describe a natural narrow stretch of sea connecting two large expanses of sea or ocean?

4 In music, from which country does the three-stringed instrument the Sham-Isen originate?

5 Was penicillin discovered by Alexander Fleming in 1925, 1928 or 1932?

6 In the USA, which state is nicknamed 'the Aloha State'?

7 Prime minister Tony Blair was a member of a band called Ugly . . . what?

8 Based in Padstow, TV chef Rick Stein specialises in what type of cookery?

9 Which G is an English opera festival that opened in 1934 with a production of Mozart's *The Marriage of Figaro*?

10 In television, in what Boston bar could you find the characters Carla Tortelli and Cliff Clayvin?

11 What type of seabird shares its name with a slang term meaning a greedy person?

12 Which composer is pictured on the reverse of a new Bank of England £20 note?

13 In television, name the actor who played the character of Lance Corporal Jones in the wartime comedy series *Dad's Army*.

14 According to legend, British rule of Gibraltar will end if what animals leave?

15 What Q is the capital city of Ecuador?

16 The 1999 film *The Insider* is based on a true story of malpractice in which industry?

17 In which sport are there events called the Vienna Regatta and the Lucern Regatta?

18 In classical music, who composed 'Clair de lune' and *La Mer*?

19 The action of James Joyce's 1922 novel *Ulysses* is inspired by which Homeric text?

20 In politics, who was the Conservative leader and prime minister in 1970?

Previous Total
1,000
800
600
450
300
200
100
50
20
Banked
Total

Answers

1 Romanov	**12** Edward Elgar
2 Europe	**13** Clive Dunn
3 Strait	**14** Apes
4 Japan	**15** Quito
5 1928	**16** Tobacco (accept cigarette)
6 Hawaii	
7 Rumours	**17** Rowing
8 Seafood (accept fish)	**18** Claude Debussy (accept Debussy)
9 Glyndebourne (Festival)	**19** The *Odyssey*
10 Cheers	**20** Edward Heath (accept Ted Heath)
11 Gannet	

Round 79

1 In what year was the first Comic Relief Red Nose Day in the UK?

2 In nature, on which tree would you find large, sticky buds with horseshoe-shaped leaf scars beneath?

3 In television, for what does BSC stand?

4 In which country are the ancient cities of Herculaneum and Pompeii?

5 Which Shakespeare play features the line 'I kiss thy hand, but not in flattery'?

6 In which 1967 film did Warren Beatty and Faye Dunaway play a pair of bank robbers?

7 On the world wide web, which country do the letters '.ca' represent?

8 In music, which successful soul group of the 1970s was founded by brothers Maurice and Verdine White?

9 In the human body, which organ stores bile after it has been produced by the liver?

10 In television, which American puppeteer created *Fraggle Rock* and *The Muppet Show*?

11 In which country might you read the *Daily Journal* newspaper in Caracas?

12 In which Rodgers and Hammerstein musical is Jud Fry killed in a knife fight with Curley, the hero?

13 The Latin phrase *'citius, altius, fortius'* is the motto for which sporting event?

14 With what profession would you associate Ozwald Boateng?

15 Traditionally, the Feast of the Epiphany is the twelfth and final day of the celebrations following Christmas. On which date does it fall?

16 What was the name of Istanbul, when it was the capital of the Eastern Roman Empire?

17 Which Thursday in Lent commemorates the day when Jesus instituted Holy Communion?

18 In film, in which year during the 1970s was the first *Godfather* film released?

19 In the human body, the bottom half of the tooth is called the root, but what is the name given to the part above the gumline?

20 In which district of south-west London has Nigel Williams set three comic novels?

Previous Total

1,000
800
600
450
300
200
100
50
20

Banked

Total

Answers

1 1988
2 Horse chestnut
3 Broadcasting Standards Council
4 Italy
5 *Julius Caesar*
6 *Bonnie and Clyde*
7 Canada
8 Earth, Wind and Fire
9 Gall bladder
10 Jim Henson
11 Venezuela
12 *Oklahoma!*
13 Olympic Games
14 Fashion (accept tailor or clothes designer)
15 6 January
16 Constantinople (do not accept Byzantium)
17 Maundy Thursday
18 1972
19 The crown
20 Wimbledon (accept SW19)

Round 80

1 In which US city would you find the Freedom Trail, a walking route marked throughout the city with a red line?

2 In a box of twelve chocolates, a third are white chocolate and the rest are milk. How many are milk chocolate?

3 Which US television company has a peacock logo?

4 In association football, how many yards apart are the goalposts?

5 What creatures does John James Audubon draw?

6 In 1968, Torquay, Paignton and Brixham merged to become what district in Devon?

7 How many countries share a border with Vietnam?

8 With which religion are Purim plays associated?

9 Carol Decker was the lead singer of which pop band?

10 In which century was the British Home Office established?

11 Who directed the 1959 film *Some Like It Hot*?

12 Who was the founder and first chancellor of the German Empire in 1871?

13 In biology, what is the name for the condition of an abnormally low body temperature in a warm-blooded animal?

14 In *EastEnders*, which of Carol Jackson's children was kidnapped after witnessing a robbery?

15 Which James Bond actor played Ivanhoe in the 1950s TV series of the same name?

16 What *E* is a type of dark hardwood traditionally used to make piano keys?

17 During which century did Christopher Marlowe write the drama *Doctor Faustus*?

18 In history, the Nineteen Propositions designed to limit the power of the crown were presented to which monarch in 1642?

19 In the animal kingdom, what is the largest mammal native to the UK, the red deer or the fallow deer?

20 Which sea creature produces the highly prized substance ambergris?

Previous Total

1,000

800

600

450

300

200

100

50

20

Banked

Total

Answers

1 Boston
2 8
3 NBC
4 8 (accept 24 feet)
5 Birds
6 Torbay
7 Three
8 Judaism (accept Jewish)
9 T'Pau
10 Eighteenth (1782)
11 Billy Wilder
12 Otto von Bismarck (accept Bismarck or Prince Bismarck)
13 Hypothermia
14 Billy
15 Roger Moore (Roger George Moore)
16 Ebony
17 Sixteenth
18 Charles I
19 Red deer
20 (Sperm) whale

Round 81

1 In human biology, what *T* is the muscular organ situated in the floor of the mouth?

2 In the film *Billy Elliot*, does Billy train to become a footballer or a ballet dancer?

3 A plant or animal in danger of extinction is described as an 'endangered . . .' what?

4 What name is given to the mainly Hebrew and Aramaic manuscripts first discovered in a cave by shepherds in 1947?

5 In musical instruments, which is bigger: a viola or a violin?

6 What *E* is the name given to the decoration of fabrics with needlework?

7 In geography, which city is closer to Birmingham: Coventry or Leicester?

8 In Greek mythology, Medusa was one of the Gorgons whose gaze could turn men into what?

9 In religion, which *Z* was the father of the apostles James and John?

10 In science, what are halogens, metallic or non-metallic?

11 Actor Henry Fonda won an Oscar for his last movie role in which 1981 film?

12 How many tiles are there in a standard mah-jong set: 124, 134 or 144?

13 In food, what is the English name of the hard Italian cheese Parmigiano?

14 In the USA, how many colonies adopted the Declaration of Independence in 1776: 10, 13 or 16?

15 In music, the word 'amp' is an abbreviation for which piece of electrical equipment?

16 In literature, in which Jane Austen novel are Mr and Mrs Bennett major characters?

17 Which sea did the ancient Romans call *Mare nostrum* or 'our sea'?

18 According to the saying, does a red sky in the morning please or upset shepherds?

19 What type of animal is a crested titmouse?

20 In children's toys, what *K* is Barbie's boyfriend?

Previous Total

1,000
800
600
450
300
200
100
50
20

Banked

Total

Answers

1 Tongue	**11** *On Golden Pond*
2 Ballet dancer	**12** 144
3 Species	**13** Parmesan
4 Dead Sea Scrolls	**14** 13
5 Viola	**15** Amplifier
6 Embroidery	**16** *Pride and Prejudice*
7 Coventry	**17** Mediterranean
8 Stone (accept rock/ statue)	**18** Upsets them – shepherd's warning
9 Zebedee	**19** A bird
10 Non-metallic	**20** Ken

Round 82

1 Which is the larger island, Trinidad or Tobago?

2 Proverbially, 'He who pays the piper calls the . . .' what?

3 In fashion, which Giorgio is an Italian fashion designer born in 1935 and renowned for his finely tailored suits?

4 In computing, what name is given to a three-dimensional interactive environment?

5 What is the general name given to an investigation by a court into disputes between employees and employers?

6 In 1977, John Travolta starred in which musical film with music by the Bee Gees?

7 What type of servant is an employee of the government and is paid by central government funds?

8 Which of these books did author L. P. Hartley *not* write: *Eustace and Hilda* or *Fly Fishing*?

9 What *B* is the short stick used by the conductor of an orchestra to direct the players?

10 A British steam engine set a new world record speed in July 1938. Was it the *Mallard* or the *Drake*?

11 In television, which soap opera, first broadcast in 1960, was created by Tony Warren?

12 Which children's writer adapted an Ian Fleming story into the film version of *Chitty Chitty Bang Bang*?

13 If the probability of a freak storm happening in a given year is four-fifths, how many storms would you expect in twenty years?

14 In history, in what year was the Riot Act passed by the British parliament, due to the Jacobite disturbances: 1715 or 1815?

15 In the animal kingdom, what G is a small, tree-dwelling ape with long arms, native to the forests of South-east Asia?

16 On which British island would you find the town of Cowes?

17 When referring to the power of a car's engine, what do the letters hp stand for?

18 In which year did independent television begin broadcasting, 1955 or 1962?

19 What US city was the original capital of America, Boston or Philadelphia?

20 Do conifer trees have separate male and female cones?

Previous Total

1,000

800

600

450

300

200

100

50

20

Banked

Total

Answers

1 Trinidad	**11** *Coronation Street*
2 Tune	**12** Roald Dahl
3 Giorgio Armani	**13** 16
4 Virtual reality	**14** 1715
5 Industrial tribunal (accept tribunal)	**15** Gibbon
6 *Saturday Night Fever*	**16** Isle of Wight
7 Civil servant	**17** Horsepower
8 *Fly Fishing*	**18** 1955
9 Baton	**19** Philadelphia
10 The *Mallard*	**20** Yes

Round 83

1 Which English city was originally a Roman outpost called Mancunium?

2 In the title of a Shakespeare play, how many gentlemen of Verona are there?

3 In the animal kingdom, which *M* is a member of the stoat family which is farmed for its thick fur?

4 Sean Connery and Ursula Andress appeared in which Bond film together?

5 Which of the famous Collins sisters has dated Warren Beatty, Joan or Jackie?

6 What *A* is the main vegetable ingredient of moussaka?

7 In nature, is the giant puffball a fungus or a sea anemone?

8 In music, the 1957 UK number one hit 'That'll Be the Day' was sung by which rock 'n' roll singer?

9 In geography, what *C* is the word used to describe a man-made waterway, either for transport or irrigation?

10 What is the common name for a type of beetle, red with black spots, that is an important destroyer of aphids?

11 In nature, which *P* is the coloured part of the flower which attracts insects?

12 In science, which produces a greater magnification, a light microscope or an electron microscope?

13 Did Hannibal and his elephants cross the Alps in AD or BC?

14 On which US sitcom did Richie Cunningham and Potsie Weber meet in Arnold's Drive-in?

15 In which country were diamonds first discovered at the town of Kimberley in the late 1860s?

16 If a rectangle's length is 6 centimetres and its width is 4 centimetres, what do all the sides add up to?

17 How many species of flying lemur are there: one, two or four?

18 Which ex-member of Yazoo went on to release 'That Ole Devil Called Love'?

19 Which Eastern European city is home to the Strahov Monastery and the Charles Bridge?

20 Does Jamaican sprinter Merlene Ottey hold an Olympic record for winning the most bronze medals or the most silver?

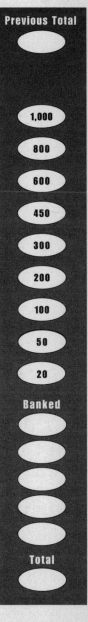

Previous Total

1,000
800
600
450
300
200
100
50
20

Banked

Total

Answers

1 Manchester	**11** Petal
2 Two	**12** Electron microscope
3 Mink	**13** BC (218 BC)
4 Dr No	**14** Happy Days
5 Joan	**15** South Africa
6 Aubergine	**16** 20 centimetres
7 Fungus	**17** Two
8 Buddy Holly	**18** Alison Moyet
9 Canal	**19** Prague
10 Ladybirds	**20** Most bronze medals

Round 84

1 According to the title of the novel by US novelist Nathaniel Hawthorne, what colour was the letter?

2 With which form of entertainment are the names Barnum and Bailey most associated?

3 The River Ganges in India is a sacred bathing place for pilgrims of which religion?

4 What *H* is a burrowing rodent with a short tail and large cheek pouches, native to Europe and North Asia?

5 The action of the 1986 film *Platoon* was set during which conflict?

6 In humans, does an antibody defend against infection or help digestion?

7 What is the name given to the salted roe of a large fish, usually the sturgeon, eaten as a delicacy?

8 Monza and Silverstone are venues for which sport?

9 What is the BBC's dedicated news channel called?

10 In science, the name of which common atmospheric gas means 'acid producer' in Greek?

11 Was Tony Blair's father a councillor for the Conservative or Labour Party?

12 In an orchestra, what is the largest and lowest-pitched of the bowed string instruments?

13 Which Norfolk town stands on the Great Ouse, near where it enters the Wash?

14 Is the kitchen utensil used to slice vegetables known as a banjo or a mandolin?

15 Which spinach-eating cartoon sailor first appeared in the comic book *Thimble Theatre* in 1929?

16 Complete the title of this 1943 novel by French author Simone de Beauvoir: *She Came to . . .* what?

17 In the animal kingdom, can hippos swim?

18 In television, Jimmy Saville presented which 1970s programme, helping to make children's dreams come true?

19 In which year did the French Revolution begin, 1779 or 1789?

20 Which English city is at the mouth of the River Wear?

Previous Total
1,000
800
600
450
300
200
100
50
20
Banked
Total

Answers

1 Scarlet	**9** BBC News 24
2 Circus	(accept News 24)
3 Hinduism (accept	**10** Oxygen
Hindu)	**11** Conservative
4 Hamster	**12** Double bass
5 The Vietnam war	**13** King's Lynn (accept
6 Defends against	Bishop's Lynn)
infection	**14** Mandolin
7 Caviar	**15** Popeye
8 Motor racing (accept	**16** *Stay*
motor sport/ Formula	**17** Yes
One/ Grand Prix	**18** *Jim'll Fix It*
racing; also accept	**19** 1789
motorcycling)	**20** Sunderland

Round 85

1 In sport, is the distance of the London Marathon just under or just over 26 miles?

2 What is the medical term for German measles?

3 If you stand at the equator facing north before noon, is your shadow to your left or right?

4 What do the letters PLC stand for when placed after a company name?

5 Acrophobia is a fear of what?

6 According to the Bohr Theory of the atom, how many electrons can the first shell of an atom hold?

7 In the Bible, which M was Noah's grandfather?

8 In theatre, what word means a collection of plays in production at one theatre in the same season?

9 In music, *An Innocent Man* and *River of Dreams* were albums made by which American singer and songwriter?

10 What P is a sport played at Cowdray Park?

11 In which decade did the space probes *Viking 1* and *Viking 2* first analyse the surface of the planet Mars?

12 How many great pyramids are situated at Giza, Egypt: two or three?

13 In biology, what D is located at the bottom of the lungs and controls the movement of air?

14 Pop star and actress Courtney Love was married to which member of the group Nirvana?

15 Which thriller writer wrote jockey Lester Piggott's official biography?

16 In what year was a regular airmail service introduced in the USA: 1908 or 1918?

17 In nature, the damsel fly is a smaller relative of which colourful insect?

18 What *R* was the name given to the payments which the 1919 Treaty of Versailles stipulated Germany must pay to the Allies?

19 Which English town on the River Orwell in East Anglia was also the birthplace of Cardinal Thomas Wolsey?

20 What *T* is the name given to a three-panel altarpiece?

Previous Total

1,000

800

600

450

300

200

100

50

20

Banked

Total

Answers

1 Over	**10** Polo
2 Rubella	**11** The 1970s (1976)
3 Left	**12** Three
4 Public Limited Company	**13** Diaphragm
5 Heights	**14** Kurt Cobain
6 Two	**15** Dick Francis
7 Methuselah	**16** 1918
8 Repertory (accept repertoire, rep)	**17** Dragonfly
9 Billy Joel	**18** Reparations
	19 Ipswich
	20 Triptych

Round 86

1 Which 1981 John Landis horror film won an Oscar for Best Make-up?

2 What term – also an architectural style – is used to describe the period from 1811 to 1820, when the Prince of Wales acted as ruler in place of his father?

3 Terry Major-Ball is the brother of which former prime minister?

4 Name the British athlete who set a new world triple jump record in 1995?

5 In geography, the Dead Sea is the lowest point of which continent?

6 Which Italian composer wrote the opera *The Barber of Seville* in 1816?

7 St Louis is the largest city in which American state?

8 Who did John F. Kennedy marry on 12 September 1953?

9 In geography, which republic lies approximately 10 miles south-west of Rimini in Italy?

10 What colour is the star on the Moroccan flag?

11 In British slang, how many pounds sterling are there in a 'pony'?

12 In geography, what dam is located in Black Canyon on the border of the US states of Nevada and Arizona?

13 Actor Jack Nicholson starred as the US president in which Tim Burton science-fiction film?

14 Which fictional detective had an older brother called Mycroft?

15 What big-selling children's doll from the 1980s celebrated its fifteen-year anniversary in the year 2000?

16 What name is given to the type of silver which is 92.5 per cent pure?

17 In history, in which American city did the gangster Al Capone build up a criminal empire?

18 Which author wrote in the preface to his only novel that 'All art is quite useless'?

19 In which TV series did Robert Vaughn play Napoleon Solo?

20 Andrea, Sharon, Caroline and Jim are the four sibling members of which Irish pop group?

Previous Total

1,000

800

600

450

300

200

100

50

20

Banked

Total

Answers

1 *An American Werewolf in London*
2 Regency
3 John Major
4 Jonathan Edwards
5 Asia
6 Rossini (accept Gioachino Rossini)
7 Missouri
8 Jacqueline Bouvier (accept Jackie Bouvier)
9 San Marino
10 Green
11 25
12 Hoover
13 *Mars Attacks!*
14 Sherlock Holmes
15 Cabbage Patch Kids
16 Sterling (silver)
17 Chicago
18 Oscar Wilde
19 *The Man from U.N.C.L.E.*
20 The Corrs

Round 87

1 What type of protein regulates the rate of chemical reaction in the body?

2 Which children's classic story contains the poems 'You are Old, Father William' and 'Beautiful Soup'?

3 Which South African city was known as Port Natal?

4 Which chairman of China's Communist Party died in 1976?

5 Which member of the England football team has written an autobiography entitled *My World*?

6 In television, what long-running science magazine programme was first presented by Raymond Baxter?

7 Which is the shortest of Shakespeare's plays?

8 Which American film composer wrote the music for the *Star Wars*, *Superman* and *Indiana Jones* films?

9 What nationality is fashion designer Alexander McQueen?

10 What is the US equivalent of Remembrance Sunday?

11 In which decade did the Cuban Missile Crisis occur?

12 In the UK, the fourth Sunday in Lent is commonly known as what?

13 In which year in the 1970s was the film *Get Carter*, starring Michael Caine, released?

14 What word describes a person who is able to use both hands with equal ease?

15 Which supermodel took a tumble on a catwalk in 1993, wearing a pair of six-inch Vivienne Westwood platform shoes?

16 The Master Cutler is an important dignatory in which city in northern England?

17 If a swimming pool is 50 metres long, how many lengths would be swum in a 2 kilometre race?

18 In television, who was the first person to chair *A Question of Sport* in 1970?

19 In which year did man first set foot on the moon?

20 Which famous gap-toothed British actor of the 1950s and 1960s was famous for his catchphrase 'An absolute shower'?

Previous Total

1,000

800

600

450

300

200

100

50

20

Banked

Total

Answers

1 Enzyme
2 *Alice's Adventures in Wonderland* (accept *Alice in Wonderland*)
3 Durban
4 Chairman Mao (accept Mao Zedong)
5 David Beckham
6 *Tomorrow's World*
7 *The Comedy of Errors*
8 John Williams (accept Williams; full name: John Towner Williams)
9 English (accept British)
10 Veteran's Day
11 1960s (1962)
12 Mothering Sunday (accept Mother's Day)
13 1971
14 Ambidextrous
15 Naomi Campbell
16 Sheffield
17 40
18 David Vine
19 1969
20 Terry-Thomas (Thomas Terry Stevens)

Round 88

1 In which English county is Kidderminster situated?

2 Which stage musical features the song 'Ol' Man River'?

3 Whose version of 'Stand by Me' was re-released as the theme to the 1986 film of the same title?

4 Corinth was an important city of which modern country?

5 In mythology, which island, housing a highly developed civilisation, is said to have been sunk beneath the waves?

6 Who directed the 1951 movie *Strangers on a Train*?

7 In biology, an amoeba is made up of how many cells?

8 In science, which metal is extracted from the metal ore bauxite?

9 In film, what was John Wayne's real name?

10 Cornish Rex and Devon Rex are both breeds of which animal?

11 Which TV programme in 1984 featured the Prince of Wales telling his own story, *The Old Man of Lochnagar*?

12 In what year in the 1940s was conscription for women introduced into Britain?

13 Which artist is known for works such as *Rain, Steam and Speed*?

14 In religion, the Islamic monument, the Dome of the Rock, is found in which Middle Eastern city?

15 In literature, what nationality was Hans Christian Andersen?

16 Which Irish-born writer said 'Life does not cease to be funny when people die any more than it ceases to be serious when people laugh'?

17 Whose first UK chart entry, '2-4-6-8 Motorway', was a top ten hit in 1977?

18 If a 150 gram jar of peanut butter contains 1,500 calories, how many calories would there be in a 50 gram jar?

19 In geography, which is the nearest major seaside resort to Lancaster and the ferry port of Heysham?

20 Born in Germany, the scientist Albert Einstein became a citizen of which country in 1940?

Previous Total

1,000

800

600

450

300

200

100

50

20

Banked

Total

Answers

1 Worcestershire
2 *Show Boat*
3 Ben E. King
4 Greece
5 Atlantis
6 Alfred Hitchcock
7 One
8 Aluminium
9 Marion Morrison (accept Marion Michael Morrison)
10 Cat
11 *Jackanory*
12 1941
13 Turner (Joseph Mallord William or J.M.W.)
14 Jerusalem
15 Danish
16 George Bernard Shaw
17 Tom Robinson
18 500 calories
19 Morecambe
20 United States (accept America)

Round 89

1 Who directed the British movie *The Devils* in 1971, starring Vanessa Redgrave and Oliver Reed?

2 *'E pluribus unum'*, meaning 'out of many, one', is the motto of which country?

3 In golf, on which course is The Masters played every year?

4 Who was the architect of the Soloman R. Guggenheim Museum in New York?

5 To which position was Joseph Goebbels appointed in 1933, under Hitler's Nazi regime?

6 How many tentacles does an octopus have?

7 Buttercup the Cow, Mrs Scrubit and Spotty Dog were characters from which 1955 children's TV programme?

8 In geography, what is the capital of the Australian state of Tasmania?

9 What type of nuts are used to make pesto?

10 Where in the British Isles is the Queen toasted as the Lord of Man?

11 In which English county is the country house Clandon Park?

12 In World War I, was the Battle of Ypres fought in France, Belgium or Germany?

13 In which British university is the Cavendish Laboratory world famous for its physics work?

14 Which English actor and author starred in *Death in Venice* in 1971?

15 In football, who managed Nottingham Forest between 1975 and 1993?

16 In which English county are Aylesbury, High Wycombe and Milton Keynes?

17 Which Australian 400 metres runner lit the Olympic flame at the Sydney 2000 games?

18 In art, the Van Gogh Museum is located in which European capital city?

19 In geography, Venezuela is on the north coast of which continent?

20 In snooker, in which decade did Cliff Thorburn make the first maximum break in the World Championships?

Previous Total

1,000
800
600
450
300
200
100
50
20

Banked

Total

Answers

1 Ken Russell
2 USA
3 Augusta National Golf Club (accept Augusta), Georgia
4 Frank Lloyd Wright
5 Minister of Propaganda
6 Eight
7 *The Woodentops*
8 Hobart
9 Pine nuts
10 Isle of Man
11 Surrey
12 Belgium
13 Cambridge
14 (Sir) Dirk Bogarde (Derek Jules Gaspard Ulric Niven van den Bogaerde)
15 Brian Clough (Brian Howard Clough)
16 Buckinghamshire (accept Bucks)
17 Cathy Freeman (Catherine Freeman)
18 Amsterdam
19 South America
20 1980s

Round 90

1 How long is an Olympic-size swimming pool: 50 metres or 100 metres?

2 A tripod and a trivet each have how many legs?

3 'There Is Nothin' Like a Dame' is a song from which musical?

4 In history, which P was president of France from 1969 until his death in 1974?

5 The term 'hepatic' relates to which organ in the body?

6 In food, what G is a sauce traditionally made with the juices of a meat that has been roasted?

7 The River Clyde runs through which Scottish city?

8 In sport, did England or Pakistan win the one-day cricket series in October 2000?

9 In science, igneous, metamorphic and sedimentary are the three main classifications of what?

10 Which Canadian actor played the lead role in the Back to the Future films?

11 In the USA, what A is the state known as the 'Heart of Dixie'?

12 In pop music, who is the lead singer of Pulp?

13 In literature, which author of the novel Jude the Obscure had a terrier called Wessex?

14 The Indian government in 1923 levied an unpopular tax on what food flavouring?

15 Ebony is the heartwood of what type of tropical trees, deciduous or evergreen?

16 In the animal kingdom, can a tiger swim?

17 In which year did the first suspended monorail open in Germany, 1901 or 1932?

18 In international weather symbols, what *D* does one comma represent?

19 Kenneth Branagh was formerly married to which English actress with whom he featured in the film *Peter's Friends*?

20 What *L* is the part of a camera through which the light from the object being photographed reaches the film?

Previous Total

1,000

800

600

450

300

200

100

50

20

Banked

Total

Answers

1 50 metres
2 Three
3 *South Pacific*
4 Pompidou (accept Georges Pompidou)
5 Liver
6 Gravy
7 Glasgow
8 Pakistan
9 Rock(s) (accept strata)
10 Michael J. Fox
11 Alabama
12 Jarvis Cocker
13 Thomas Hardy
14 Salt
15 Evergreen
16 Yes
17 1901
18 Drizzle (do *not* accept rain)
19 Emma Thompson
20 Lens

Round 91

1 The film *Tommy* in 1975 was a rock opera written by Pete Townshend, a member of which band?

2 Which A is the part of a car's engine which generates electricity to charge the battery?

3 In British politics, does the Charter 88 group believe in protecting the status quo or in the process of reform?

4 Which British racecourse is the venue for a four-day royal meeting each June?

5 Was J. S. Bach's music composed in the Romantic or the Baroque era?

6 In TV, what was the name of the tweed-coated puppet fox whose catchphrase was 'Boom-boom'?

7 In the natural world, what L are areas of water separated from the open sea by reefs?

8 What nationality was the writer and poet James Joyce?

9 In a class of 20 pupils, four-fifths are girls. How many are boys?

10 In history, the Restoration refers to the re-establishment of what in Britain?

11 In the animal kingdom, which W is a small carnivorous mammal related to the stoat?

12 Is the Tropic of Capricorn in the northern or southern hemisphere?

13 What T is a dark brown or black viscous liquid formed from a mixture of distilled coal, shale and wood?

14 In 1964, which TV channel began broadcasting in Britain?

15 Do endothermic reactions release or absorb energy?

16 In the TV comedy series *The New Statesman*, who played Alan B'stard?

17 In the children's book *Alice's Adventures in Wonderland*, which animal is pictured wedged in the teapot?

18 Which leading actor would you associate with the films *Sleepless in Seattle* and *Big*?

19 In music, was the Beatles' *Revolver* album released in 1964, 1966 or 1968?

20 In TV, which children's animation features a black and white cat called Jess?

Previous Total

◯

1,000

800

600

450

300

200

100

50

20

Banked

◯
◯
◯
◯
◯

Total

◯

Answers

1 The Who	**11** Weasel
2 Alternator	**12** Southern
3 Reform	**13** Tar
4 Ascot	**14** BBC2
5 Baroque	**15** Absorb
6 Basil Brush	**16** Rik Mayall
7 Lagoons	**17** Dormouse
8 Irish	**18** Tom Hanks
9 Four	**19** 1966
10 The monarchy (accept Charles II/ the king)	**20** *Postman Pat*

Round 92

1 Which Mexican alcoholic spirit is made from a cactus-like plant called the agave?

2 The 1787 Constitution of the USA was drafted by 55 delegates known as the Founding . . . what?

3 Which country and western singer's biggest UK hit was 'Stand By Your Man' in 1975?

4 If you were in Algiers, in which country would you be?

5 In nature, do frog tadpoles develop their front or back legs first?

6 In medicine, is astigmatism a defect of the heart or the eye?

7 In radio and television, what A is a device which improves reception?

8 In television, which sitcom featured the characters Norman Stanley Fletcher and Lennie Godber and was set in a prison?

9 In politics, General Augusto Pinochet headed which country's military government from 1973 to 1990?

10 According to the proverb, what is mightier than the sword?

11 The US industrialist Henry Ford founded his company in 1903, manufacturing what?

12 The town of Newbury is in which English county?

13 If the length of a rectangle is 5 centimetres and the width is 3 centimetres, what do all the sides add up to?

14 In food, what dish has a Spanish–American name meaning 'chilli with meat'?

15 In food, what M is an airy, crisp confection of beaten egg white and sugar?

16 In the animal kingdom, does the crab-eating fox eat only crabs?

17 In pop music, which group had their first UK number one single in 1967 with the song 'Massachusetts'?

18 Which football team is known as The Owls: Sheffield Wednesday or Sheffield United?

19 In the USA, the chain of islands and reefs between the Straits of Florida and Florida Bay are known as the Florida . . . what?

20 In literature, which of these was the title of a Samuel Richardson novel: *Marissa*, *Clarissa* or *Patricia*?

Previous Total

1,000

800

600

450

300

200

100

50

20

Banked

Total

Answers

1 Tequila	**11** Automobiles (accept cars/motors)
2 Fathers	
3 Tammy Wynette	**12** Berkshire
4 Algeria	**13** 16 centimetres
5 Back	**14** Chili con carne
6 Eye	**15** Meringue
7 Aerial (accept antenna)	**16** No
	17 Bee Gees
8 Porridge	**18** Sheffield Wednesday
9 Chile	**19** Florida Keys
10 The pen	**20** *Clarissa*

Round 93

1 In the UK, with which form of entertainment is the name Billy Smart associated?

2 It is a duty of observant followers of which religion to make a pilgrimage to Mecca?

3 What is the opposite of the medical condition alkalosis?

4 In television, name the nineties sitcom about fashion which was born out of a French and Saunders sketch.

5 Was entertainer Bob Hope born in England or the US?

6 What *H* is a type of crab that has a soft unprotected abdomen and inhabits portable hollow objects?

7 In politics, do the initials TD after someone's name indicate a Member of Parliament in the Republic of Ireland or Scotland?

8 Which *P* is a length of board or fabric used to hide a curtain rod?

9 In food, Pentland Crown, Red King and Kerr's Pink are all varieties of which vegetable?

10 What chain of shops did Anita Roddick open in 1976?

11 In nature, which *P* are large treeless plains in South America?

12 Which country scuppered its own fleet at Scapa Flow rather than hand it over to the enemy at the end of World War I?

13 In what year was the League of Nations established by the Versailles Peace Settlement: 1919 or 1939?

14 Complete the title of this 1992 John Grisham novel: *The Pelican . . .* what?

15 What *A* is a swift-running deer-like animal with upward-pointing horns, with species such as beira and golden?

16 In the nursery rhyme 'Sing a Song of Sixpence', who had her nose pecked off by a blackbird?

17 Which African country did Italy invade in 1935, Abyssinia or the Sudan?

18 Which conflict involving Britain was the subject of the Franks Report, published in 1983?

19 On which river does the English city of Cambridge stand?

20 What *H* describes the offspring of two unrelated animals or plants?

Previous Total

1,000
800
600
450
300
200
100
50
20

Banked

Total

Answers

1 Circus	**12** Germany
2 Islam (accept Muslim/ Mohammedism)	**13** 1919
	14 *Brief*
3 Acidosis	**15** Antelope
4 *Absolutely Fabulous*	**16** The maid
5 England	**17** Abyssinia
6 Hermit crab	**18** Falklands Conflict (accept Falklands War)
7 Republic of Ireland	
8 Pelmet	**19** River Cam (accept Granta)
9 Potato	
10 The Body Shop	**20** Hybrid
11 Pampas	

Round 94

1 In which country are the ski resorts of Verbier, Klosters and St Moritz?

2 Complete the title of this 1979 film: *Tarka the* . . . what?

3 In nature, which is larger, a stoat or a polecat?

4 What A is the verb meaning to improvise a speech or piece of music without preparation?

5 In the TV cartoon, what is the name of Homer and Marge Simpson's eldest child?

6 Were electric lights first used on the White House Christmas tree by President Grover Cleveland or Theodore Roosevelt?

7 What O is the final part of the Space Shuttle to return to Earth?

8 Is the horse-racing town of Newmarket situated in Suffolk or Cambridgeshire?

9 In music, with which British pop star did Aretha Franklin duet on the 1987 hit 'I Knew You Were Waiting For Me'?

10 In sport, for which country did brothers Henry and Robbie Paul play in the 2000 Rugby League World Cup?

11 On what river would you find the English city of Peterborough?

12 In chemistry, cobalt is one of the three commonest magnetic metallic elements. Name one of the other two.

13 In history, which V were seafaring warriors who raided and colonised wide areas of Europe from the ninth to the eleventh centuries?

14 In fashion, what kind of garment is a baldric?

15 Which P were Biblical people who inhabited five cities including Ashdod and Gaza?

16 Which author, with the first name Muriel, wrote the novel *The Prime of Miss Jean Brodie*?

17 Which of the Wright brothers manned the first powered flight, Wilbur or Orville?

18 In marine life, do rays have bones?

19 What nationality was the polar explorer Roald Amundsen?

20 In biology, what E is the study of the relationship between organisms and their environments?

1,000

800

600

450

300

200

100

50

20

Banked

Total

Answers

1 Switzerland	**11** Nene
2 Otter	**12** Iron, nickel
3 Polecat	**13** Vikings
4 Ad lib	**14** Belt/sash
5 Bart Simpson	**15** Philistines
6 Grover Cleveland	**16** (Muriel) Spark
7 Orbiter	**17** Orville
8 Suffolk	**18** No (they are
9 George Michael	cartilaginous)
(Yorgos Panayiotou)	**19** Norwegian
10 New Zealand	**20** Ecology

Round 95

1 In Greek mythology, how many Titans were there, seven or twelve?

2 Craig Douglas, Ringo Starr and Billy Idol have all had UK hit songs about girls of what age?

3 In film, which actor played a doctor in love with a married woman in the 1940s film *Brief Encounter*?

4 In history, Sylvia and Christabel were the daughters of which Manchester-born suffragette?

5 In geology, what M is a line of rock debris carried and deposited by an advancing glacier?

6 With which sport would you associate Bernie Ecclestone?

7 In which city could you see Canada's Parliament Buildings?

8 The name of which percussion instrument comes from the German for 'bells' and 'play'?

9 In science, what name is given to any chemical compound containing only hydrogen and carbon?

10 In the Bible, which was the first bird to be released from the ark?

11 In the USA, on which day of the week is Thanksgiving celebrated?

12 Which spiky-haired Aston Villa-supporting violinist made his debut with the Philharmonia Orchestra in 1977?

13 What *P* is the name of the port which serves the city of Athens?

14 Who managed the England football team for the World Cup group match against Finland in October 2000?

15 In geography, which American bay is entered from the Pacific Ocean by the Golden Gate strait?

16 Pygmy, alpine and water are three types of which small mammal?

17 In biology, otitis is an inflammation of which part of the human body?

18 What 1990s BBC sitcom featured characters revived from *Are You Being Served*?

19 With which other English poet did Samuel Coleridge publish *Lyrical Ballads* in 1798?

20 Which city is the principal sea port of Argentina?

Previous Total

( )

(1,000)

(800)

(600)

(450)

(300)

(200)

(100)

(50)

(20)

Banked

( )
( )
( )
( )
( )

Total

( )

Answers

1 Twelve	**11** Thursday
2 Sixteen	**12** (Nigel) Kennedy
3 Trevor Howard	**13** Piraeus
4 Mrs (Emmeline) Pankhurst	**14** Howard Wilkinson
5 Moraine	**15** San Fransisco (Bay)
6 Formula 1 (accept motor racing)	**16** Shrew
7 Ottawa	**17** The ear
8 Glockenspiel	**18** *Grace and Favour*
9 Hydrocarbon	**19** (William) Wordsworth
10 Raven	**20** Buenos Aires

Round 96

1 In nature, firs, cedars, larches and spruces are all members of which group of trees?

2 Which British actress starred as Gudrun in Ken Russell's 1969 film adaptation of *Women in Love*?

3 Which adventurer is Paul Hogan renowned for playing?

4 Which Polish-born composer lived with novelist George Sand?

5 The fictional politician Francis Urquhart features in *House of Cards*, a novel by which British author?

6 Who led the Labour government from 1945 to 1951?

7 In 1976, with which song did Brotherhood of Man win the Eurovision Song Contest?

8 In Shakespeare's *The Merchant of Venice*, Portia's suitors chose from three caskets. The first was made of gold, the second silver; from what was the third made?

9 Which US state takes its name from a British king and was the thirteenth British colony?

10 The British film *The Full Monty* is set in which town?

11 In which year were The Rolling Stones formed?

12 Who is the author of the Wombles story books?

13 Which South Korean city was originally called Hanyang, then Kyongsong?

14 Whom did Ronald Reagan defeat when he was elected president of the US in 1980?

15 In which year did Mother Teresa die?

16 Which fish grows to maturity in fresh water before going to the Sargasso Sea to spawn?

17 Which *Blackadder* star also wrote the 1989 children's TV series *Maid Marian and Her Merry Men*?

18 How many days does a heptathlon last?

19 In fashion, to which member of the royal family has Sir Hardy Amies been dressmaker by appointment since 1952?

20 What is the name of the Scottish outdoor gathering that includes caber-tossing, dancing and bagpipe-playing?

Previous Total

( )

1,000

800

600

450

300

200

100

50

20

Banked

( )
( )
( )
( )
( )

Total

( )

Answers

1 Pine (accept conifers/evergreen)
2 Glenda Jackson
3 Crocodile Dundee (accept Mick Dundee/Croc Dundee)
4 Chopin (Frédéric Chopin)
5 Michael Dobbs
6 (Clement) Attlee
7 'Save Your Kisses for Me'
8 Lead
9 Georgia
10 Sheffield
11 1962
12 Elizabeth Beresford
13 Seoul
14 Jimmy Carter (accept Carter, President Carter, James Earl Carter Junior, etc.)
15 1997
16 (Freshwater) eels (*anguilliformes*, or *anguillidae*)
17 Tony Robinson
18 Two
19 The Queen (Elizabeth II)
20 The Highland Games

Round 97

1 'Varicella' is the Latin for which disease that chiefly affects children and is caused by a virus of the herpes group?

2 What band set a record in 1996 when all three singles they released got to number one in that year?

3 Which Daphne du Maurier novel is narrated by the unnamed second wife of Maxim de Winter?

4 The River Irwell forms the boundary between Salford and which other northern city?

5 In maths, what *I* is a triangle that has two sides of equal length?

6 In television, which drama situated around a boatyard featured a character called Jan Howard?

7 Which British hurdler was the first woman to win gold medals in Olympic, World, Commonwealth and European games?

8 In which pantomime does Robin Hood usually appear?

9 What *M* is the name given to a bar which divides a window vertically?

10 In medicine, what name is given to the study and treatment of cancer?

11 In which Irish county are the Mountains of Mourne?

12 In the animal kingdom, leopards and jaguars are both what kind of cat?

13 Spurn Head is located at the mouth of which river?

14 What was the surname of Busby, who transformed the Hollywood musical with his kaleidoscopic choreography?

15 Which boy-girl pop band released the album *Steptacular*?

16 In British history, who commanded the English Parliamentary army in the Civil War?

17 Which ancient Egyptian god was the god of the sun?

18 In which decade was the Disney film *Bambi* released?

19 Which term, popularised by Arnold Toynbee, describes the economic and manufacturing development in England in the eighteenth and nineteenth centuries?

20 In human biology, what *H* is released during an allergic reaction?

Previous Total

1,000

800

600

450

300

200

100

50

20

Banked

Total

Answers

1 Chicken pox	**13** River Humber (accept Humber, Humber estuary)
2 Spice Girls	
3 *Rebecca*	
4 Manchester	**14** Berkeley (accept Enos)
5 Isosceles	
6 *Howard's Way*	**15** Steps
7 Sally Gunnell	**16** Oliver Cromwell
8 *Babes in the Wood*	**17** Ra (accept Re)
9 Mullion	**18** 1940s (accept forties) (1942)
10 Oncology	
11 County Down	**19** Industrial revolution
12 Panther	**20** Histamine

Round 98

1 How many players are there in a volleyball team?

2 Who directed the 1968 science-fiction film *2001: A Space Odyssey*?

3 Schipperkes and Schnauzers are breeds of what?

4 The Soviet Union was at war with which Scandinavian country from 1939 to 1940, and from 1941 to 1944?

5 Which twentieth-century poet's first published collection was entitled *Prufrock and Other Observations*?

6 A sumo wrestler weighs 0.2 metric tons. How much is this in kilograms?

7 In which English town was the first Roman colony in Britain based?

8 Which artist was born in East Bergholt, Suffolk on 11 June 1776?

9 In what decade did the first module for the International Space Station go into orbit?

10 In the TV series, Ally McBeal works for a law firm in which American city?

11 In nature, hooded and carrion are the two native British species of which bird?

12 Jim Moir is the real name of which anarchic British comedian who presented the 1990s TV shows *Big Night Out* and *Shooting Stars*?

13 In cricket, who captained England during their series victory over the West Indies in 2000?

14 The Volkswagen, launched in 1936 by Adolf Hitler, was designed by Ferdinand who?

15 What name is given to a semicircular window over a door?

16 In mythology, who killed Achilles at Troy?

17 What is the dark dead wood in the centre of a tree trunk called?

18 Which 1940s film starring Cary Grant, Katharine Hepburn and James Stewart was reworked into a musical version, *High Society*?

19 How many teeth should an adult human have: 30, 32 or 34?

20 In sport, which football team plays home games at Filbert Street stadium?

Previous Total

1,000

800

600

450

300

200

100

50

20

Banked

Total

Answers

1 Six
2 Stanley Kubrick
3 Dog
4 Finland
5 T. S. Eliot (accept Thomas Stearns Eliot)
6 200 kg
7 Colchester (accept Camulodunum)
8 John Constable (accept Constable)
9 Nineties (1998)
10 Boston
11 Crow
12 Vic Reeves
13 Nasser Hussain
14 Porsche
15 Fanlight (US: transom)
16 Paris
17 Heartwood (accept duramen)
18 *The Philadelphia Story*
19 32
20 Leicester City

Round 99

1 Which English river does the Queen Elizabeth II Bridge cross?

2 In pop music, which female group had a UK number one hit with 'Stop! In the Name of Love', The Three Degrees or The Supremes?

3 Which *M* is a condiment made with olive oil, vinegar, egg yolk and seasoning?

4 Is the Japanese flag white with a red circle or red with a white circle?

5 In what Russian city did Lenin practise as a lawyer before becoming a revolutionary?

6 In what sport do you have inside- and outside-centres, locks and flankers?

7 In medicine, what *H* is a term used to describe abnormally high blood pressure?

8 What is the name of the highest point in Greece?

9 According to Genesis, did the land of Nod lie to the east or the west of the Garden of Eden?

10 In children's television, on what common did the Wombles live?

11 In the nineteenth century, which Protestant evangelical and charitable organisation was founded by William Booth?

12 In literature, John Steinbeck was awarded the Pulitzer Prize in 1940 for which novel?

13 What B is the amount of computer memory needed to store a single character?

14 Complete the title of this 1979 film starring Dustin Hoffman and Meryl Streep: *Kramer . . .* what?

15 In the USA, which political party is nicknamed the 'Grand Old Party'?

16 In the British peerage, which is the higher degree of nobility, knight or baronet?

17 What was Irish singer Chris De Burgh's biggest-selling hit single?

18 Flamenco is a style of music originating from which country?

19 What B is a farm building used for the storage of cereal crops and hay?

20 In the animal kingdom, which is the larger, the great white or the whale shark?

1,000
800
600
450
300
200
100
50
20

Banked

Total

Answers

1 Thames
2 The Supremes
3 Mayonnaise
4 White with a red circle
5 St Petersburg
6 Rugby Union (accept rugby, *do not* accept Rugby League)
7 Hypertension
8 Mount Olympus
9 East
10 Wimbledon Common
11 Salvation Army
12 *The Grapes of Wrath*
13 Byte
14 *Versus Kramer*
15 Republican Party (accept Republicans)
16 Baronet
17 'Lady in Red'
18 Spain
19 Barn
20 Whale shark

Round 100

1 What is the name of Ralph Lauren's clothing company, which shares its name with an equestrian sport?

2 In what year was *Space Invaders* launched in the UK, 1978 or 1982?

3 Complete the title of this 1986 David Lynch film: *Blue . . .* what?

4 Which F is the part of a plant that contains the seeds?

5 Which party is represented by the initials SNP?

6 Which Scottish football manager said 'If Everton were playing at the bottom of the garden, I'd pull the curtains', Bill Shankly or Kenny Dalglish?

7 In classical music, who composed the *Messiah* and *Music for the Royal Fireworks*?

8 On an Ordnance Survey map, what animal represents a zoo?

9 On what 1980s TV series did Geordie builders Oz, Neville and Dennis seek employment on a German building site?

10 Which cathedral is taller, Salisbury or Truro?

11 Which American author wrote the travelogue *The Lost Continent*?

12 In maths, are polygons two-dimensional shapes or three-dimensional shapes?

13 In fashion, with which items of clothing is designer Jimmy Choo associated?

14 In ancient history, what *V* was the volcano which erupted in AD 79, destroying Pompeii?

15 In nature, what is the common name for the group of birds known as raptors, such as hawks and eagles?

16 In geography, Stratford-upon-Avon is in which English county?

17 What was the real first name of landscape gardener 'Capability' Brown: Tarquin or Lancelot?

18 What *A*, derived from Plato's School of Philosophy, describes an association of artists, scholars or musicians?

19 Who was the first, newly elected, American president of the twentieth century?

20 What *A* is a device on which rows of beads are used to make calculations?

Previous Total

1,000
800
600
450
300
200
100
50
20

Banked

Total

Answers

1 Polo	**11** Bill Bryson
2 1978	**12** Two-dimensional
3 *Velvet*	**13** Shoes
4 The fruit	**14** Vesuvius
5 Scottish National Party (accept Scottish Nationalists)	**15** Birds of prey
	16 Warwickshire
	17 Lancelot
6 Bill Shankly	**18** Academy
7 Handel (George Friedrich Handel)	**19** Theodore Roosevelt (in 1901)
8 Elephant	**20** Abacus (accept abacuses)
9 *Auf Wiedersehen Pet*	
10 Salisbury	

Round 101

1 In cooking, what *F* is a French word describing a dish that is covered in alcohol and set alight?

2 In which Scottish city can you go trainspotting at Waverley Station?

3 In which decade was the ex-Soviet president Mikhail Gorbachev born, the 1930s or the 1940s?

4 In which 1989 film did Bruce Willis provide the voice of the character Mike-Ee?

5 Which sitcom won an award for Most Popular Comedy at the National Television Awards 2000?

6 In food, what *T* is an expensive form of fungus, considered a delicacy?

7 In music, what is the name of singer Mel B's baby daughter?

8 Is Nigeria north or south of the equator?

9 What type of fish, often caught by children, has a series of elongated spines on its back to deter predators?

10 In medicine, does Addison's disease affect the adrenal gland or the pituitary gland?

11 In ancient history, how many Punic Wars were fought in the second and third centuries BC: two, three or four?

12 Launched on 4 October 1957, what was the name of the first spacecraft to orbit the Earth?

13 In television, which Raymond Briggs animated Christmas story features a song entitled 'Walking in the Air'?

14 Which former British Prime Minister is the most famous old boy of Rutlish School, Merton Park, South London?

15 In art, which *B* is a metal frequently used in cast sculptures?

16 The Channel Tunnel car terminal is directly next to which Kent port?

17 Add 30 to the square root of 49.

18 In the animal kingdom, what *H* is the name given to a female deer?

19 In music, Benny and Björn from the pop group Abba collaborated with Tim Rice on which musical?

20 In which century did construction of the Notre Dame cathedral in Paris begin: the eleventh or twelfth?

Previous Total

1,000

800

600

450

300

200

100

50

20

Banked

Total

Answers

1 Flambé	**11** Three
2 Edinburgh	**12** *Sputnik One* (accept
3 1930s (1931)	*Sputnik*)
4 *Look Who's Talking*	**13** *The Snowman*
5 *The Royle Family*	**14** John Major
6 Truffle	**15** Bronze
7 Phoenix Chi	**16** Folkestone
8 North	**17** 37
9 Stickleback	**18** Hind
(Gasterosteidae)	**19** *Chess*
10 Adrenal gland	**20** Twelfth (1163)

Round 102

1 In literature, in which Charles Dickens novel does Betsy Trotwood feature?

2 Which entrepreneur founded the Virgin company, selling records by mail order?

3 The US city of Sacramento is the capital of which state?

4 In theatre, Henry Irving was the first actor to receive what honour in 1895?

5 In nature, do mosses and liverworts flower?

6 In the animal kingdom, is an otter a herbivore or a carnivore?

7 In religion, what is the name of the independent state which is the spiritual and administrative home of the Roman Catholic Church?

8 Which member of the Collins family wrote the book *The Bitch*?

9 In human biology, what part of the body does the ciliary muscle control?

10 In art, what *P* is the term for applying a thin layer to the base to make the surface more suitable for painting?

11 Which British female designer won Designer of the Year at the *Vogue* fashion awards in New York in October 2000?

12 In musical instruments, how many strings does a violin have?

13 Which is the local government centre of Essex, Colchester or Chelmsford?

14 In nature, what O is a tree that has clusters of pale brown buds and produces acorns as its fruit?

15 In pop music, who duets with Kylie Minogue on her new album, *Light Years*?

16 In cookery, which creamy leek and potato soup is usually served cold?

17 Which TV presenter has fronted *Newsnight* and *University Challenge*?

18 What E was a World War II coding machine, whose codes were thought by the Germans to be unbreakable?

19 On which side of the road do cars drive in the Republic of Ireland?

20 In the animal kingdom, what B is a two-humped camel?

Previous Total

1,000

800

600

450

300

200

100

50

20

Banked

Total

Answers

1 *David Copperfield*	**11** Stella McCartney
2 Richard Branson	**12** Four
3 California	**13** Chelmsford
4 Knighthood	**14** Oak
5 No	**15** Robbie Williams
6 Carnivore	**16** Vichyssoise
7 Vatican City (accept the Vatican)	**17** Jeremy Paxman
8 Jackie (Collins)	**18** Enigma
9 The eye (accept lens)	**19** Left
10 Priming	**20** Bactrian

Round 103

1 When was *Blue Peter* first broadcast, 1952 or 1958?

2 In history, Prussia ceased to exist as a German state after which World War?

3 Which MP and fomer actress resigned her post in 1999 so that she could campaign to be Mayor of London?

4 In which French city could you see the original of the *Venus de Milo* statue?

5 In music, 'Hello', 'Say You Say Me' and 'All Night Long' were hits for which American soul singer?

6 Which British racing-car manufacturing company was started by Frank Williams in 1969?

7 In the Bible, in the first Book of Samuel, who killed the Philistine giant Goliath?

8 What S is a device commonly used by doctors to listen to sounds within a patient's body?

9 A vaporetto is a waterbus associated with which Italian city?

10 Was the 1960s film *A Taste of Honey* a British, American or Scandinavian film?

11 What A is an amusing account of an incident?

12 Name either of the two sons of King George V who came to the British throne.

13 Do hedgehogs have the ability to swim?

14 What populated archipelago is situated in the Atlantic Ocean about 32 land miles off mainland Cornwall?

15 What *A* is the branch of physics that deals with sound and sound waves?

16 'The iron' is the nickname for which piece of safety equipment in the theatre?

17 What *HD* is a famous US motorcycle manufacturing company founded in 1903?

18 Who, in the year 2000, became the first golfer since Ben Hogan in 1953 to win three successive majors?

19 What *A* is the name given to a robot that resembles a human being?

20 Over how many years did Germany originally agree to pay reparations following World War I, 27 or 42 years?

Answers

1 1958
2 The Second (World War II)
3 Glenda Jackson
4 Paris (in the Louvre)
5 Lionel Richie
6 Williams
7 David
8 Stethoscope
9 Venice
10 British
11 Anecdote
12 Edward VIII and George VI (also accept David and Albert – names they were known by before accession)
13 Yes
14 Scilly Isles (accept Scillies/Isles of Scilly)
15 Acoustics
16 Safety curtain (accept fireproof curtain)
17 Harley-Davidson
18 Tiger Woods
19 Android (accept automaton)
20 42 years

Round 104

1 Does the current Duke of Edinburgh need a passport to travel abroad?

2 What *E* is the process used to preserve a body from decay, that was used widely by ancient Egyptians?

3 Is Ben Oldfield or Bruce Oldfield a famous UK fashion designer?

4 Which northern English city has two cathedrals, both built in the twentieth century?

5 In which century was the English poet and artist William Blake born?

6 Is there such a thing as a flower-faced bat?

7 Which women's Christian name was shared by two wives of Henry VIII and the wife of Shakespeare?

8 Who was the Roman god of doors, gateways and beginnings?

9 Who is the singer and lead guitarist in the rock band Dire Straits?

10 Humphrey Bogart and Lauren Bacall starred in which 1946 film adapted from a Raymond Chandler thriller?

11 What do the initials of the European Union policy of CAP stand for?

12 Which *T* is a small freshwater turtle often kept as a pet?

13 In sewing, French, box and concertina are types of what?

14 Which family of musical instruments is Evelyn Glennie famous for playing?

15 An oxide of which gas is represented by the formula NO_2?

16 What *A* is a modern synthetic paint which allows a combination of oil and watercolour techniques?

17 What do Americans call a drawing pin?

18 Which former child star of the *Home Alone* films made his West End stage debut in the play *Madame Melville* in October 2000?

19 How many commercial airports serve London?

20 At the Sydney Olympics, which African country won gold in the men's football tournament?

Previous Total

1,000

800

600

450

300

200

100

50

20

Banked

Total

Answers

1 Yes
2 Embalming (accept embalmment)
3 Bruce
4 Liverpool
5 Eighteenth century (1757)
6 Yes
7 Anne
8 Janus
9 Mark Knopfler
10 *The Big Sleep*
11 Common Agricultural Policy
12 Terrapin
13 Pleat (accept pleats)
14 Percussion (accept drums)
15 Nitrogen
16 Acrylic
17 Thumbtack
18 Macaulay Culkin
19 Five (Stanstead, Luton, Heathrow, Gatwick, City)
20 Cameroon

Round 105

1 In 1962, *Cover Her Face* was the first novel by which female crime writer?

2 In the animal kingdom, silk, for commercial textile use, is produced from the cocoon of which insect?

3 In geography, which island republic lies 185 miles south-east of Greenland?

4 In film, who starred in *From Here To Eternity* in 1953 and the 1962 movie *The Birdman of Alcatraz*?

5 The wife of novelist Aldous Huxley typed up part of the manuscript of *Lady Chatterley's Lover* for which author?

6 What was the trade of comedian Paul Whitehouse before writing for Harry Enfield and Vic Reeves?

7 In which country might you spend a dinar in Amman?

8 Which former member of The Goons presented a children's TV show called *Potty Time*?

9 In which stadium do Scotland play their home rugby internationals?

10 On the world wide web, which country is represented by the letters '.de'?

11 With which area of medicine is Franz Mesmer associated?

12 Which city was the capital of New Zealand before Wellington became the capital in 1865?

13 In which century was the original Globe Theatre at Southwark built?

14 Who directed the films *Shallow Grave*, *Trainspotting* and *The Beach*?

15 Which European country was condemned in 1973 for exploding several nuclear devices in the South Pacific?

16 Which virtuoso jazz saxophonist, who died in 1955, was known by the nickname 'Bird'?

17 By what name was China known to the West in medieval times?

18 Which medical problem is commonly called 'pink eye'?

19 In which century was the escapologist Harry Houdini born?

20 In literature, William Golding is best known for which novel about schoolboys marooned on a desert island?

Previous Total

1,000

800

600

450

300

200

100

50

20

Banked

Total

Answers

1 P. D. James (Phyllis Dorothy James White)
2 Silk moth (accept moth/worm/silkworm/ mulberry silk moth)
3 Iceland
4 Burt Lancaster (Burton Stephen Lancaster)
5 D. H. Lawrence
6 Plasterer
7 Jordan
8 Michael Bentine
9 Murrayfield (accept the Murrayfield Stadium)
10 Germany
11 Hypnotism (accept mesmerism/ mesmerise)
12 Auckland
13 Sixteenth (1599)
14 Danny Boyle
15 France
16 Charlie Parker (accept Charles Christopher Parker Jnr)
17 Cathay
18 Conjunctivitis
19 Nineteenth (1874)
20 *Lord of the Flies*

Round 106

1 If a 250 gram jar of jam contains 1250 calories, how many calories are there in a 100 gram jar?

2 In the TV crime series *The Sweeney*, John Thaw played Reegan. Who played Carter?

3 In the animal kingdom, do giant pandas hibernate?

4 In animal biology, which system do the brain and spinal cord form?

5 In geography, Rap-Anewee, a Chilean island famous for its huge rock sculptures of heads, is also known as what?

6 In mythology, what *F* were the Roman goddesses of vengeance?

7 Who directed the 1974 detective film *Chinatown*?

8 Who was the general secretary of the Communist Party of the Soviet Union between 1985 and 1991?

9 What is tennis star Billie-Jean King's maiden name?

10 In science, what does the term UHF stand for?

11 In television, the children's programme *The Clangers* featured armour-plated mouse-like creatures. Who created them?

12 What type of weapon was a Trident that was fitted to US and British submarines in the 1980s and 1990s?

13 Which famous racing figure owns Sinndar, winner of the 2000 Derby and Prix de l'Arc de Triomphe?

14 In literature, in which decade did George Orwell write *Nineteen Eighty-Four*?

15 In pop music, whose army gave Elvis Costello his biggest UK singles chart success in 1979?

16 In maths, what is the square root of 64?

17 From which country does the bongo drum originate?

18 The town of Milford Haven is in which country in the UK?

19 According to the proverb, if you can't ride two horses at once, you shouldn't be in the . . . what?

20 In astronomy, what is the name given to a star system composed of two stars?

Previous Total

◯

1,000

800

600

450

300

200

100

50

20

Banked

◯

◯

◯

◯

◯

Total

◯

Answers

1 500 calories
2 Dennis Waterman
3 No
4 Central nervous system (accept CNS)
5 Easter Island
6 Furies (accept *Furiae*)
7 Roman Polanski
8 Mikhail Gorbachev
9 Moffitt
10 Ultra-high frequency
11 Oliver Postgate
12 (Nuclear) missile (accept intercontinental ballistic missile)
13 Aga Khan
14 1940s
15 Oliver's
16 8
17 Cuba
18 Wales
19 Circus
20 Binary star

Round 107

1 The Skydome is found in which Canadian city?

2 In geography, is Beachy Head situated nearer Hastings or Eastbourne?

3 Which member of the royal family is mother to Peter and Zara Phillips?

4 In the children's TV series *The Magic Roundabout*, what was the name of the dog?

5 In history, in which month in 1805 did the Battle of Trafalgar take place: October or November?

6 What C is a dry, white sparkling wine produced in France and usually drunk on special occasions?

7 Former England manager Bobby Robson is the manager of which Premiership football club?

8 In the Christian Bible, does Leviticus appear in the Old or New Testament?

9 In the nursery rhyme that starts 'Hey diddle diddle', which piece of cutlery did the dish run away with?

10 In science, what B is a type of gas burner, commonly used in laboratories?

11 Which American city is known as 'The Big Apple'?

12 Is Malibu located on America's east or west coast?

13 In the animal kingdom, a Great Dane is what kind of animal?

14 In which rock band did Phil Collins sing and play drums from 1970 to 1995?

15 In ancient literature, which A is a Greek philosopher who wrote the *Poetics*?

16 In which year was the Women's Peace Camp established outside Greenham Common: 1981 or 1985?

17 In nature, what B is a hole or tunnel dug by a small animal as a home?

18 In geography, which ocean is surrounded by the 'Ring of Fire', the Atlantic or Pacific?

19 In the life cycle of the butterfly, what comes after the egg and before the pupa?

20 In what year did graduates of the Open University first receive their degrees: 1965 or 1973?

Previous Total

1,000

800

600

450

300

200

100

50

20

Banked

Total

Answers

1 Toronto
2 Eastbourne
3 Princess Anne (Princess Royal)
4 Dougal
5 October
6 Champagne (*do not* accept cava – Spanish)
7 Newcastle United
8 Old Testament (accept Old)
9 The spoon
10 Bunsen burner
11 New York
12 West
13 Dog
14 Genesis
15 Aristotle
16 1981
17 Burrow
18 Pacific
19 Larva
20 1973

1 In nature, do dragonflies have a sting?

2 What C is a type of soft, light wool from the hair of an Asian goat?

3 At approximately what speed does the Earth travel round the sun? 16,000 miles an hour or 66,000 miles an hour?

4 What R is the name for a thin slice of bacon?

5 What A is the name given to the male head or superior of a monastery or abbey?

6 What 1985 film was the last to star Roger Moore as James Bond?

7 Of which part of the UK is Plaid Cymru the nationalist party?

8 In which Canadian city is the Gilles Villeneuve Grand Prix motor-racing circuit, Quebec or Montreal?

9 Which conductor fronted the Promenade concerts from 1948 up to his death in 1967?

10 In medicine, what H is the name given to the condition of an abnormally low level of sugar in the blood?

11 Which broadcaster provided the world's first daily public television service?

12 What nationality is fashion designer Jean-Paul Gaultier?

13 In nature, is pollen the male or female cell of seed plants?

14 If a cyclist travels at 15 miles per hour, how long will it take him to cycle 90 miles?

15 In geography, the Exmoor National Park is located in Somerset and which other English county?

16 What name is given to a floating mass of ice, of which 80 per cent is usually under water?

17 In which century was the world's first passenger railway built, the eighteenth or nineteenth?

18 Which British TV game show featured the character Dusty Bin?

19 In the USA, were there more Republican or Democrat presidents in power during the twentieth century?

20 In art, what *P* is a writing material prepared from the marsh plant of the same name?

Previous Total

1,000

800

600

450

300

200

100

50

20

Banked

Total

Answers

1 No	**11** BBC
2 Cashmere	**12** French
3 66,000 mph	**13** Male
4 Rasher	**14** Six hours
5 Abbot	**15** Devon
6 *A View to a Kill*	**16** Iceberg
7 Wales	**17** Nineteenth (1806)
8 Montreal	**18** *Three Two One*
9 Sir Malcolm Sargent	**19** Republican
10 Hypoglycaemia	**20** Papyrus

Round 109

1 The Sears Tower in Chicago is one of the world's tallest buildings, with how many storeys? 110 or 210?

2 In film, which American actor would you associate with *The French Connection* and *Mississippi Burning*?

3 What A was the fleet of 130 ships sent by Philip II of Spain to invade England in 1588?

4 The initials MSG stand for which food additive?

5 Which chat show won the award for Most Popular Programme at the National Television Awards 2000?

6 In which continent is the River Gambia?

7 Which ex-wife of Andrew Lloyd Webber had several hits in the 1980s with songs from his musicals?

8 In human biology, does the thorax refer to the head or the chest?

9 Which famous space agency was created in America in 1958?

10 What type of insect transmits yellow fever?

11 In television, Larry Hagman starred in which US sitcom about a beautiful blonde genie?

12 In politics, who did John Major make deputy prime minister in 1995?

13 What name is given to the conflict between England and France which ran between the 1330s and 1450s?

14 In maths, how many right angles does a rectangle have?

15 In nature, what A are plants that live in the sea or in lakes, and have no roots, leaves or flowers?

16 Which member of The Beatles had sons called Sean and Julian?

17 East and West Germany were officially reunified after 45 years as separate nations in which year: 1980 or 1990?

18 With which actor do you associate the catchphrase 'Not a lot of people know that'?

19 In which sport might a competitor perform a 'hiplock' or a 'flying mare'?

20 In clothing, did the poncho originate in Africa or South America?

Previous Total

1,000

800

600

450

300

200

100

50

20

Banked

Total

Answers

1 110
2 Gene Hackman
3 Armada
4 Monosodium glutamate
5 *Parkinson*
6 Africa
7 Sarah Brightman
8 The chest
9 NASA (National Aeronautics and Space Administration)
10 Mosquito
11 *I Dream of Jeannie*
12 Michael Heseltine
13 Hundred Years War
14 Four
15 Algae
16 John Lennon
17 1990
18 Michael Caine
19 Wrestling
20 South America

Round 110

1 In Shakespeare's *A Midsummer Night's Dream*, who is the servant of the king of the fairies?

2 Is the city of Milwaukee situated in the state of Wisconsin or Montana?

3 What *M* is a type of lily that shares its name with a famous female pop star?

4 Complete the title of this Tennessee Williams play: *A Streetcar Named . . .* what?

5 The winner of which golf competition has received a silver claret jug since 1872?

6 In biology, does the artery carry blood away from or towards the heart?

7 In theatre, which *F* is the name applied to a comedy play dealing with an absurd situation?

8 What is the name of the eccentric Spanish painter who went to the opening of the 1936 Surrealist Exhibition wearing a diving suit?

9 What was the title of the fly-on-the-wall documentary following life at St James's Hospital in Leeds?

10 In computing, what *I* is a small picture on a computer screen that represents a specific function?

11 In which Jane Austen novel is Mr Woodhouse the heroine's father?

12 What did the Tremeloes say is 'golden' in the title of their 1967 UK singles hit?

13 Which fashion designer introduced the so-called New Look in 1947?

14 Is kabuki a form of theatre originating in Japan or Korea?

15 Name the son of Kingsley Amis who wrote *Time's Arrow* and *Night Train*.

16 In the animal kingdom, are snakes herbivores or carnivores?

17 Complete the title of the Stephen Sondheim musical: *A Little Night . . .* what?

18 Which city did the Romans call Deva: Chester or Chichester?

19 Is a waltz written in triple or quadruple time?

20 In which decade was the independent environmental protection organisation Greenpeace founded?

Previous Total
1,000
800
600
450
300
200
100
50
20
Banked
Total

Answers

1 Puck (accept Robin Goodfellow)
2 Wisconsin
3 Madonna lily (accept Madonna)
4 *Desire*
5 British Open (accept The Open)
6 Away from
7 Farce
8 Salvador Dalí (accept Salvador Felipe Jacinto Dalí y Domenech)
9 *Jimmy's*
10 Icon
11 *Emma*
12 Silence
13 Christian Dior
14 Japan
15 Martin (Amis)
16 Carnivores
17 *Music*
18 Chester
19 Triple time
20 1970s

Round 111

1 In human biology, what *A* is the name given to the mass of lymphoid tissue behind the nose?

2 Which famous artist is credited with sketching and designing a helicopter in 1483?

3 In what year was the Football Association formed, 1863 or 1903?

4 If you were at Malpensa Airport, in which Italian city would you be?

5 What is the traditional method of working out the age of a tree?

6 Name the actress who plays Ally McBeal in the American TV series of the same name.

7 In science, in which century was the periodic table devised, the seventeenth or nineteenth?

8 Which *B* wrote the play *Mother Courage and her Children*?

9 Name the boy band who had worldwide success with the song 'Mmm-Bop'.

10 In sport, is the game of squash played with a racket, a bat or a cue?

11 In chemistry, what kind of liquids are aqua regia and vitriol?

12 What political party was first founded in Britain in 1973 under the name of the Ecology Party?

13 In nature, is amber a fossilised resin from trees or insects?

14 In the human body, what is the medical name for the windpipe?

15 In American politics, in what decade did the Watergate scandal occur?

16 Which former *Byker Grove* actress has presented *MTV* and *The Big Breakfast*?

17 In literature, were Shakespeare's sonnets dedicated mainly to a man or a woman?

18 Which dynasty ruled China from 1368 to 1644?

19 In what year was the first electronic hearing aid invented, 1893 or 1923?

20 In mythology, what creature was part man, part horse?

Previous Total

1,000
800
600
450
300
200
100
50
20

Banked

Total

Answers

1 Adenoids	**9** Hanson
2 Leonardo da Vinci (accept Leonardo/da Vinci)	**10** Racket
	11 Acids
	12 The Green Party
3 1863	**13** Trees
4 Milan	**14** The trachea
5 Counting its rings (seen in the cross-section of the trunk) (accept dendrochronology)	**15** 1970s
	16 Donna Air
	17 A man
	18 Ming
6 Calista Flockhart	**19** 1923
7 Nineteenth	**20** A centaur
8 Bertolt Brecht (accept Brecht)	

Round 112

1 Is Cape Verde in Senegal the most easterly or most westerly point in Africa?

2 From what kind of pastry are chocolate eclairs and profiteroles made?

3 Who repeated her Broadway performance as Fanny Brice in the 1968 film version of *Funny Girl*?

4 In history, James Madison was the fourth president of the USA in which century, the eighteenth or nineteenth?

5 There are two main political parties in the Irish Republic. One is Fine Gael. What is the other?

6 Which European city staged the Winter Olympics for the second time in 1976?

7 What is the art and practice of drawing maps called?

8 In the animal kingdom, what is the tusked wild ancestor of the domestic pig?

9 In music, for how many performers is a septet composed?

10 In geological history, what period followed the Triassic period and preceded the Cretaceous?

11 Which book of the Bible records the death of Moses?

12 In which US state is Fort Knox?

13 If you were at Schipol Airport, in which European city would you be?

14 Which English football club has won the European Cup and the Cup Winners' Cup, but not the UEFA Cup?

15 How many countries share a border with Iraq?

16 Which poetry-writing detective made his first appearance in *Cover Her Face* in 1962?

17 On what 1990s British TV game show did competitors complete challenges in the Aztec, medieval and industrial zones?

18 In the animal kingdom, by what name is the African ant bear better known?

19 In geography, which country was formerly known as Persia?

20 In the 1996 film *The Rock*, Nicolas Cage had to rescue hostages from which landmark prison?

Previous Total

1,000

800

600

450

300

200

100

50

20

Banked

Total

Answers

1 Westerly
2 Choux
3 Barbra Streisand
4 Nineteenth (1809-17)
5 Fianna Foil
6 Innsbruck
7 Cartography
8 Wild boar (accept boar)
9 Seven
10 Jurassic
11 Deuteronomy
12 Kentucky
13 Amsterdam
14 Manchester United
15 Six
16 Adam Dalgliesh (accept Detective Chief Inspector/ Superintendant/Chief Superintendant Adam Dalgliesh)
17 *The Crystal Maze*
18 Aardvark
19 Iran
20 Alcatraz

Round 113

1 In music, which Italian operatic composer wrote *Rigoletto* in 1851?

2 Who wrote the original Sherlock Holmes stories?

3 Which theatrical impresario brought *Les Misérables* and *Miss Saigon* to the West End?

4 In money, what is the highest-value British banknote ever issued?

5 In television, which playwright wrote the drama *Boys from the Blackstuff*?

6 In art, what is the first name of the English landscape painter, Turner?

7 Which Victorian novelist wrote *Bleak House*, first published in book form in 1853?

8 What is the real first name of the actor Sean Connery?

9 Which girl band won the Outstanding Contribution to British Music Award at the Brits 2000?

10 By what name was Ethiopia formerly known?

11 What is the family name of brothers Harry, Albert, Jack and Sam, who moved from owning cinemas to making films in 1923?

12 Which BBC comedy series is set in the fictitious village of Royston Vaisey?

13 By what first name was the German composer Wagner, born in Leipzig in 1813, known?

14 Who attended a football match in Rome for the first time as part of the celebrations of the Third Christian Millennium?

15 According to tradition, which type of worker is said to bring good luck at a wedding?

16 What is the name given to the act of making a person, place or thing holy and sacred?

17 Which actor starred in the films *All the President's Men* and *Out of Africa*?

18 What part of the body is normally examined by a reflexologist?

19 Out of 24 boys in a class, three-quarters of them have brothers. How many boys do *not* have brothers?

20 Which avenue in New York is regarded as the centre of America's advertising industry?

Previous Total

1,000
800
600
450
300
200
100
50
20

Banked

Total

Answers

1 Giuseppe Verdi (accept Verdi)
2 Arthur Conan Doyle (accept Conan Doyle)
3 Cameron Mackintosh
4 £1,000
5 Alan Bleasdale
6 Joseph
7 Charles Dickens
8 Thomas
9 Spice Girls
10 Abyssinia
11 Warner (Warner Brothers)
12 *The League of Gentlemen*
13 Richard
14 Pope John Paul II (accept the Pope)
15 Chimney sweep
16 Consecration (accept consecrating)
17 Robert Redford
18 Feet (accept feet and hands)
19 Six
20 Madison (Avenue)

Round 114

1 What *D* is the medical term for indigestion?

2 The 1969 production of the film *Goodbye, Mr Chips* starred which 1960s pop star as Katherine Bridges?

3 The Flemings and the Walloons are native peoples of which European country?

4 In which year of the 1980s did Michael Jackson release the album *Thriller*?

5 In the nursery rhyme, what was the murder weapon with which the sparrow killed Cock Robin?

6 Which flamboyant singer and actress starred as Mrs Flax in the 1990 film *Mermaids*?

7 In which country was the music box invented in the 1790s?

8 Which number is associated with the parallel that divides North and South Korea: the 38th or 56th?

9 The term 'zoo' is an abbreviation of what word?

10 In food, with which religion is the dish of the gefilte fish associated?

11 In baseball, what is the name of the series of matches played to decide the overall major league champion team?

12 What was the original name of Sellafield Nuclear Power Station in Cumbria?

13 Which film actress is the younger sister of Olivia de Havilland?

14 Which surname was shared by television's famous rag-and-bone men and a test-tube baby pioneer?

15 Where was the British code and cipher school which cracked the Enigma codes based: Bletchley Park or Blenheim Palace?

16 In Islam, who – with the help of his son, Ismail – built the Kaaba in Mecca?

17 Which footballing organisation celebrated its centenary in 1988?

18 In children's literature, who wrote the *Mr Men* series of books?

19 Is a hurdy-gurdy a type of cake or a musical instrument?

20 How long is the diagonal of a rectangle measuring 12 centimetres by 5 centimetres? 13 or 18 centimetres?

Previous Total

1,000

800

600

450

300

200

100

50

20

Banked

Total

Answers

1 Dyspepsia
2 Petula Clark
3 Belgium
4 1982
5 Bow and arrow (accept arrow)
6 Cher
7 Switzerland
8 38th
9 Zoological (accept zoological gardens)
10 Judaism (accept Jewish)
11 The World Series
12 Windscale
13 Joan Fontaine
14 Steptoe
15 Bletchley Park
16 Ibrahim (accept Abraham)
17 The Football League
18 Roger Hargreaves
19 Musical instrument
20 13 centimetres

Round 115

1 In music, who sang 'Bright Eyes', the theme to the 1978 animated film *Watership Down*?

2 Which partly fictionalised book by Alex Haley traced his ancestry back to Africa?

3 In the proverb, what shouldn't one meet halfway?

4 Which seventeenth-century English mathematician and physicist is known for his laws on motion and gravity?

5 Which *Coronation Street* actress played Cleopatra in the film *Carry On Cleo*?

6 Which coin gives its name to a pub game involving pushing discs on a marked board?

7 In television, who starred as Ricky Ricardo alongside his real-life wife, Lucille Ball, in the US sitcom *I Love Lucy*?

8 In the animal kingdom, the alpaca, gwen-arco and vicuna are all close relatives of which other South American animal?

9 In which year did presenter Zoe Ball marry DJ Norman Cook?

10 The Very Large Array, a radio telescope centre, is located in Socorro in which American state?

11 Who was Edward III talking about when he said 'Let the boy win his spurs'?

12 What is the surname of Louisa May Alcott's *Little Women*?

13 What is the name of the US Stock Exchange average, calculated and published daily?

14 Which US novel by Alice Walker, set in the Deep South, won the Pulitzer Prize in 1983?

15 In the TV comedy series *Birds of a Feather*, Sharon and Tracy are sisters. What is the first name of their man-hungry neighbour?

16 What is the name given to a castrated cock fowl fattened for eating?

17 Who did Henry McLeish succeed as leader of the Scottish Labour Party in October 2000?

18 Name the American actor, born in 1936, who starred in *Easy Rider* and *Blue Velvet*.

19 The St Valentine's Day Massacre of 1929 occurred in which American city?

20 Who helped draft the American Declaration of Independence, before becoming the second president of the US in 1797?

Previous Total

1,000

800

600

450

300

200

100

50

20

Banked

Total

Answers

1 Art Garfunkel	**12** March
2 *Roots*	**13** Dow Jones (accept Dow Jones indices or index)
3 Troubles	
4 Sir Isaac Newton	
5 Amanda Barrie	**14** *The Color Purple*
6 Halfpenny (Shove Ha'penny)	**15** Dorien (Dorien Green)
	16 Capon
7 Desi Arnaz	**17** Donald Dewar
8 Llama	**18** Dennis Hopper
9 1999	**19** Chicago
10 New Mexico	**20** John Adams
11 Black Prince (accept Prince Edward/his son)	

Round 116

1 By what name was the actress Norma Jean Baker better known?

2 In 1896, what was the in-town speed limit in Britain, 2 mph or 5 mph?

3 Which Scottish football team plays home games at the Ibrox Stadium?

4 What is the predominant flavour of the liqueur crème de cacao?

5 For what purpose was the Taj Mahal originally erected – as a mausoleum or as a wedding gift?

6 The White Cliffs are situated beside which English port?

7 In the animal kingdom, is there such an animal as the star-nosed mole?

8 What were Susan, Sugar and Heather, who all have their graves at Sandringham?

9 What is half of 310?

10 In physics, are diesel and petrol engines internal or external combustion engines?

11 In medicine, yellowing of the skin or whites of the eyes is a symptom of what J?

12 In the USA, 'Uncle . . . *what*' is the nickname of the American government, probably coined during the war of 1812?

13 What *T* is the name given to the art of decorating the skin using a needle and permanent dye?

14 In pop music, 'Dance to the Music' was a 1968 UK hit for Sly and the Family . . . what?

15 What is the name of the longest river in France?

16 In food, what *B* is an organism fermented with milk to make yoghurt?

17 In what year did US pilot Chuck Yeager become the first man to fly faster than the speed of sound – 1947 or 1962?

18 What was invented in the late eighteenth century by John Spilsbury, when he stuck a map of England onto a piece of wood and cut it up?

19 What *F* is the fertilised ovary of a flower?

20 In which TV sitcom did Michele Der-Treece star as Betty Spencer?

Previous Total

1,000

800

600

450

300

200

100

50

20

Banked

Total

Answers

1 Marilyn Monroe
2 2 mph
3 Glasgow Rangers (accept Rangers)
4 Chocolate (accept cocoa)
5 Mausoleum
6 Dover
7 Yes
8 Royal corgis (accept dogs or the Queen's pets)
9 155
10 Internal (combustion engines)
11 Jaundice
12 Uncle Sam (accept Sam)
13 Tattooing (accept tattoo)
14 Stone
15 The Loire
16 Bacteria
17 1947
18 Jigsaw puzzle
19 Fruit
20 *Some Mothers Do 'Ave 'Em*

Round 117

1 In the animal kingdom, does a cheetah's pregnancy last three to four months, or seven to eight months?

2 In geography, in which ocean would you find the Gulf Stream?

3 What *R* are a Black religious and political group originating in the 1920s in Jamaica?

4 In language, what is the name for an academic term in the United States?

5 Which German driver, who has a brother named Ralph, won the 2000 Formula One World Championship?

6 In science, do alkalis have a pH number greater or lower than seven?

7 Is a busby a hat traditionally worn by a soldier or a sailor?

8 Which British airport opened on 1 January 1946 as London's new civil airport?

9 In medicine, what *G* is a thin woven material used for the preparation of dressings?

10 Other than Chinese, what is the official language of Hong Kong?

11 In television, which famous crime-fighting duo of the 1970s and 1980s were played by David Soul and Paul Michael Glazer?

12 In literature, what *K* is an adventure novel written by Robert Louis Stevenson?

13 In maths, how many equal sides does a rhombus have?

14 In history, did Hannibal – who marched across the Alps to attack Rome – die in 183 BC or 183 AD?

15 In the animal kingdom, what is a kookaburra?

16 In which English county would you find Lincoln and Skegness?

17 In which sport do the spectators walk down the pitch to tread in the divots at half-time?

18 In medicine, what is the word 'flu' short for?

19 Which Y is a country on the Arabian Peninsula formed in 1990 by the union of two adjacent states?

20 The first ten amendments to the USA Constitution are collectively known as the Bill of . . . what?

Previous Total

1,000

800

600

450

300

200

100

50

20

Banked

Total

Answers

1 Three to four (months)
2 Atlantic
3 Rastafarians (accept Ras Tafari)
4 Semester
5 Michael Schumacher
6 Greater
7 Soldier
8 Heathrow
9 Gauze
10 English
11 Starsky and Hutch
12 *Kidnapped*
13 Four
14 (183) BC
15 A bird (accept kingfisher/laughing jackass)
16 Lincolnshire
17 Polo
18 Influenza
19 Yemen
20 Rights

Round 118

1 In fashion, which *E* is a shoe with a rope-covered sole?

2 In literature, complete the title of this Thomas Hardy novel from 1874: *Far From the* . . .

3 The artist Claude Monet was best known for paintings of which type of flower?

4 Which David Lean film starring Omar Sharif and Julie Christie was a worldwide hit in 1965?

5 In literature, according to Shelley, is hell a city much like London or Paris?

6 Which TV comedian's catchphrase was: 'It's all done in the best possible taste'?

7 In cookery, how is gazpacho soup usually served, hot or cold?

8 Television presenter Jools Holland used to play the keyboards in which band: Squeeze or Stretch?

9 In biology, in which century did the scientist William Harvey describe the heart as a pump?

10 Which American film star married Swansea-born actress Catherine Zeta-Jones in November 2000?

11 In the UK, is the underground village Skara Brae on the Orkney Islands or the Hebrides?

12 On what TV game show were contestants told 'Say what you see'?

13 In politics, in which year were the Scottish Parliament and Welsh Assembly established?

14 What *L* is deposited when hard water boils?

15 In which Scottish city are Union Street, Castlegate and Mercat Cross?

16 In religion, how many Sundays are there in Advent?

17 According to custom, at the Up-Helly-Aa festival in Lerwick, do they burn a guy, a ship or a haystack?

18 Which female American pop-singing diva shares her surname with a city in Texas?

19 In sport, which Gateshead-born runner broke the world record for both the 1500 metres and the mile within eleven days in 1985?

20 In religion, what *Z* is a form of Buddhism?

Previous Total

1,000

800

600

450

300

200

100

50

20

Banked

Total

Answers

1 Espadrille	**10** Michael Douglas
2 *Madding Crowd* (do not accept *Maddening*)	**11** Orkney Islands
	12 *Catchphrase*
	13 1997
3 Water lilies	**14** Limescale
4 *Dr Zhivago*	**15** Aberdeen
5 London	**16** Four
6 Kenny Everett	**17** A (Viking) ship
7 Cold	**18** Whitney Houston
8 Squeeze	**19** Steve Cram
9 Seventeenth	**20** Zen

Round 119

1 What K is the name of the inner soft part of a nut or seed?

2 In the New Testament, on which day of the week did Christ first appear to his disciples after his resurrection?

3 On which famous London street is the Vaudeville Theatre to be found?

4 In the human body, what type of blood vessels carry blood back to the heart?

5 Which of the following artists was born last: Michelangelo, Raphael or Leonardo da Vinci?

6 In TV, Margaret Rutherford and Joan Hickson both starred as which of Agatha Christie's sleuths?

7 By what acronym is radio detection and ranging more commonly known?

8 In what year was the first in-flight movie shown on an aeroplane, 1925 or 1947?

9 In classical music, are lieder songs or dances?

10 In which London borough is the Millennium Dome situated?

11 Did New Order or New Edition top the UK charts in 1983 with 'Candy Girl'?

12 In food, what F is the Greek name for a pastry dough of many paper-thin layers, separated by films of butter?

13 Name the Liverpudlian DJ who was part of the 1967 opening of Radio 1 and became renowned for creating stars in his *Late Night Sessions*.

14 In which year was it announced that the USSR had developed its own atom bomb, 1945 or 1949?

15 In art, is an odalisque a painting of a man or a woman?

16 What *E* is a large-winged bird of prey found in many mountainous regions worldwide?

17 What is the name of the female villain in the 1961 Disney film *101 Dalmatians*?

18 In government, what does MOD stand for?

19 What is the nickname given to the major increase in the annual birth rate in the UK following the end of World War II?

20 What *V* is the name given to a person who abstains from eating meat?

Previous Total

◯

1,000

800

600

450

300

200

100

50

20

Banked

◯

◯

◯

◯

◯

Total

◯

Answers

1 Kernel
2 Sunday (accept 'the first day of the week')
3 The Strand
4 Veins
5 Raphael
6 Miss Marple
7 Radar
8 1925
9 Songs
10 Greenwich
11 New Edition
12 Filo
13 John Peel
14 1949
15 Woman
16 Eagle
17 Cruella De Ville
18 Ministry of Defence
19 Baby Boom
20 Vegetarian (accept vegan)

Round 120

1 In sport, is judo Chinese or Japanese in origin?

2 In law, what *l* is an inquiry held by a coroner into an unexplained death?

3 On vehicles from which country are the letters 'ZW' displayed to identify their nationality?

4 In which northern city is the Crucible Theatre?

5 In film, Doris Day starred as the title character alongside Howard Keel in which 1953 musical?

6 Which strait lies between Alaska and Russia?

7 In marine life, do sperm whales have teeth?

8 According to the proverb, pride goes before a . . . what?

9 In television, who presented *Animal Magic* and is best remembered for providing the animals' voices?

10 Is the element strontium named after a Scottish village or a Swedish scientist?

11 In theatre, what do you call a speech at the start of a play made by one of the characters or an actor representing the playwright?

12 In pop music, what is the real first name of Baby Spice?

13 Which city hosted the first Summer Olympic games after the Second World War?

14 What two things are the same length when an equinox occurs?

15 In which decade was the wreck of the luxury liner the *Titanic* discovered, the 1980s or 1990s?

16 In the human body, which *E* is the organ in the body responsible for the control of balance?

17 In geography, is a cataract a type of waterfall, ocean current or glacier formation?

18 Which stage musical features 'The Lambeth Walk'?

19 In literature, who wrote the novel *Birdsong*, William Faulkner or Sebastian Faulks?

20 Name the location in Tombstone, Arizona where, in 1881, Wyatt Earp and his three brothers took part in a famous gunfight.

Previous Total

1,000

800

600

450

300

200

100

50

20

Banked

Total

Answers

1 Japanese	**11** Prologue
2 Inquest	**12** Emma
3 Zimbabwe	**13** London
4 Sheffield	**14** Day and night
5 *Calamity Jane*	**15** 1980s (1985)
6 Baring Strait	**16** Ear
7 Yes	**17** Waterfall
8 Fall	**18** *Me and My Girl*
9 Johnny Morris	**19** Sebastian Faulks
10 Scottish village	**20** OK Corral

Round 121

1 The manatee is a large marine mammal commonly known as what: the sea cow or sea horse?

2 What establishments became universities under the 1992 Higher and Further Education Act?

3 Which American actor played Mitch McDeere in the 1993 film *The Firm*?

4 What *A* is the science of travel through the Earth's atmosphere?

5 In politics, what *U* is used to describe a perfect society?

6 In music, which Lennon and McCartney song mentions Edgar Allan Poe and the Eggman?

7 In Arthurian legend, which knight of the Round Table was the son of Lancelot and Elaine?

8 According to the verse, 'In fourteen hundred and ninety-two, . . .' *who* 'sailed the ocean blue'?

9 In politics, what did the letters GLC stand for?

10 In golf, which country won the 2000 Alfred Dunhill Cup, Spain or South Africa?

11 How many standard bottles of champagne are in a jeroboam?

12 What *C* is the prestigious New York concert hall that opened in 1891?

13 Graphology is the study of what?

14 In American politics, the holder of which political office is also Commander-in-Chief of the Armed Forces?

15 In UK rail transport, for what do the initials of the organisation SRA stand?

16 Which popular 1950s singer had a backing group called The Crickets?

17 In which Mediterranean country would you find the summer tourist resort of Agia Napa?

18 Which voracious fish with razor-sharp teeth is native to the Amazon River?

19 In finance, what tax might you have to pay on profits made when you sell assets such as shares?

20 A horse is measured in hands. How many inches are in a hand?

Answers

1 Sea cow	**13** Handwriting
2 Polytechnics	**14** The president
3 Tom Cruise	**15** Strategic Rail Authority
4 Aeronautics	**16** Buddy Holly
5 Utopia	**17** Cyprus
6 'I Am The Walrus'	**18** Piranha (South
7 Sir Galahad	American rivers
8 Columbus (accept	generally, but mainly
Christopher Columbus)	associated in people's
9 Greater London	minds with the
Council	Amazon)
10 Spain	**19** Capital Gains Tax
11 Four	(accept CGT)
12 Carnegie Hall	**20** Four

Round 122

1 Which British singer and songwriter hosted and performed a charity concert at the last ever event at Wembley Stadium in November 2000?

2 In which 1957 film did Henry Fonda play a dissenting juror trying to convince the others that the case was not as it seemed?

3 In football, the FA Premier League champions play the winners of what trophy annually for the Charity Shield?

4 Who wrote the operetta *The Pirates of Penzance*?

5 In British business, for what do the letters OFT stand?

6 The young of what animal are called leverets?

7 In literature, which American author wrote *The Old Man and the Sea*?

8 In television, what was the name of the tiny inhabitants of Knotty Ash, created by Ken Dodd?

9 In history, how many English kings have been called Henry?

10 In literature, which American writer and poet wrote the short story 'The Fall of the House of Usher', published in 1839?

11 Which British actor was best known for his Oscar-winning performance as Professor Higgins in the 1964 film *My Fair Lady*?

12 In astronomy, the sun is mainly made up of helium and which other gas?

13 In which country are the world's largest oil reserves?

14 In theatre, which M is a puppet controlled by attached rods and wires?

15 Which Russian-born American composer wrote the *musicals Annie Get Your Gun* and *Call Me Madam?*

16 In the Christian religion, what is the name of the ritual by which people are admitted to the priesthood?

17 In the human body, which P describes the muscular movement of food through the gut?

18 How old was Elvis Presley when he died?

19 In literature, which British author wrote the novels *Day of the Triffids* and *The Chrysalids?*

20 Chicago is a city in which American state?

Previous Total

1,000

800

600

450

300

200

100

50

20

Banked

Total

Answers

1 (Sir) Elton John	**9** Eight
2 *Twelve Angry Men*	**10** Edgar Allan Poe
3 FA Cup	**11** Rex Harrison
4 Gilbert and Sullivan (accept William Schwenk Gilbert and Sir Arthur Seymour Sullivan)	**12** Hydrogen
	13 Saudi Arabia
	14 Marionette
	15 Irving Berlin
	16 Ordination
5 Office of Fair Trading	**17** Peristalsis
6 Hare	**18** 42
7 Ernest Hemingway	**19** John Wyndham
8 The Diddymen	**20** Illinois

Round 123

1 If an athlete did 100 press-ups every day, how many would he do in a non-leap year?

2 On what 1980s TV game show did competitors have to propel an egg over a set distance without breaking it?

3 In which decade was the British actor Sir Peter Ustinov born, the 1920s or 1930s?

4 What is the name of the Australian swimmer nicknamed the 'Thorpedo'?

5 A lapidary is an expert at cutting and polishing what?

6 In which limb would you find the radius bone?

7 When applied to a type of aircraft, what do the initials STOL stand for?

8 How many horns does the black rhino have?

9 Lee and H are the only male members of which pop band?

10 In history, George Patton was an American general during which world war?

11 In Greek mythology, what H was the ruler of the underworld?

12 When a country or region is surrounded by land on all sides, with no access to the sea, what is it said to be?

13 Which actor starred as King Arthur opposite Vanessa Redgrave in the 1967 film *Camelot*?

14 Which kitchen appliance uses radiation in the short-wave region of the electromagnetic spectrum?

15 In the TV series *Coronation Street*, who is played by Bill Tarmey?

16 What type of creature is a Camberwell beauty?

17 Which 1987 film, directed by Steven Spielberg, tells the story of the Second World War through the eyes of a child?

18 What was the name of the general who led Spanish Nationalists to victory in the 1936 to 1939 Spanish Civil War?

19 Who retired as a footballer with Newcastle in 1984, then returned as manager eight years later?

20 In children's literature, who wrote *Puck of Pook's Hill* in 1906 and *Rewards and Fairies* in 1910?

Previous Total

1,000

800

600

450

300

200

100

50

20

Banked

Total

Answers

1 36,500
2 *The Great Egg Race*
3 1920s (1921)
4 Ian Thorpe
5 Jewels
6 Arm
7 Short take-off and landing
8 Two
9 Steps
10 The World War II
11 Hades
12 Landlocked
13 Richard Harris
14 Microwave oven (accept microwave)
15 Jack Duckworth
16 Butterfly
17 *Empire of the Sun*
18 Franco
19 Kevin Keegan
20 Rudyard Kipling

Round 124

1 In humans, what *I* is the inability to fall asleep?

2 What is the name of Elvis Presley's grand home in Memphis, Tennessee?

3 In food, what *T* is a large bird commonly cooked at Christmas?

4 In which year were canned baked beans in tomato sauce first introduced to Britain: 1901 or 1923?

5 In the animal kingdom, is a baby panda called a cub or a kitten?

6 In motor racing, would you find Mika Hakkinen in a car or on a motorbike?

7 In the UK, which airport is further west, Heathrow or Gatwick?

8 Which one of the following is *not* practised in ballroom dancing: the foxtrot, tango or macarena?

9 Is the North Pacific Current warm or cold?

10 In martial arts, is kendo practised using bamboo swords or bare hands?

11 Will Smith, Bill Pullman and Jeff Goldblum starred in which science-fiction film about an alien invasion of Earth?

12 What is the name of Dana Scully's partner in the science-fiction TV series *The X Files*?

13 In the United States, is the majority of Death Valley National Park situated in Nevada or California?

14 In food, a galia is a type of which fruit?

15 In literature, which character created by Washington Irving fell asleep in the Catskill Mountains for twenty years?

16 In what year did the first full-sized supermarket open in Britain: 1948 or 1958?

17 Useful materials such as wood, oil and coal are collectively called 'natural . . .' what?

18 In the animal kingdom, what type of animal is an ibis?

19 In the Bible, in the book of Revelation, what A is the site of the final battle between Good and Evil?

20 Is Mount Kilimanjaro an active or inactive volcano?

Previous Total

1,000

800

600

450

300

200

100

50

20

Banked

Total

Answers

1 Insomnia
2 Graceland (Mansion)
3 Turkey
4 1901
5 Cub
6 Car (Formula One)
7 Heathrow
8 Macarena
9 Warm
10 Bamboo swords
11 *Independence Day*
12 (Fox) Mulder (*do not* accept David Duchovny)
13 California
14 Melon
15 Rip Van Winkle
16 1948
17 Resources (accept fuels)
18 Bird (accept wading bird)
19 Armageddon
20 Inactive

Round 125

1 If a grasshopper covers a horizontal distance of 5 centimetres in one jump, how many jumps will it take to cover a metre?

2 A 'liquorice stick' is a nickname for which musical woodwind instrument?

3 In science, what word is short for light amplification by stimulated emission of radiation?

4 In which decade was the famous Biba boutique opened?

5 Was Roy Lichtenstein an artist or a philosopher?

6 Who played the title role in the 1959 film *Ben-Hur*?

7 Are the Great Bear and Great Slave Lakes situated in Australia or Canada?

8 In politics, who is the wife of a former Labour leader who was elected MEP for Wales in 1999?

9 In snooker, who holds the record for most World Championship titles, Stephen Hendry or Steve Davis?

10 What S is the name for sacred writings believed to be divinely inspired?

11 Which city on the French–German border is the seat of the Council of Europe and European Court of Human Rights?

12 Mel Smith and which other member of the *Not The Nine O'Clock News* team starred in the comedy show *Alas Smith and Jones*?

13 In the title of the 1946 film, how many times does the Postman Always Ring?

14 What would your phone bill be if you made 100 calls at a cost of 4.4 pence each?

15 For how many years did the House of Normandy reign in England, 69 or 89?

16 According to the proverb, what shouldn't you teach your grandmother to suck?

17 What name is given to the distance travelled by a beam of light in space in one year?

18 Radio City Music Hall opened in December 1932 in which American city?

19 In science, is an insulator a good or a bad conductor of heat?

20 Did India achieve independence from England before or after World War II?

Previous Total

1,000

800

600

450

300

200

100

50

20

Banked

Total

Answers

1 20
2 Clarinet
3 Laser
4 1960s (accept sixties) (1964)
5 Artist
6 Charlton Heston
7 Canada
8 Glenys Kinnock
9 Stephen Hendry
10 Scriptures (accept scripture)

11 Strasbourg
12 Griff Rhys Jones
13 Twice
14 440 pence or £4.40
15 69
16 Eggs
17 A light year
18 New York
19 Bad
20 After (in 1947)

1a A hippophile is a lover of which animal?

1b In what year did Britain sign the Maastricht Treaty?

2a Which English dame made her first appearance on the stage as Viola in the Oxford University Dramatic Society's 1952 production of *Twelfth Night*?

2b In religion, what is the name given to the liberation of the people of Israel from slavery in Egypt, under the leadership of Moses?

3a In which John Ford film does John Wayne's character go looking to avenge his niece's abduction?

3b For what do the initials of J. K. Rowling – author of the Harry Potter books – stand?

4a What two letters are used to determine whether a reactant is dissolved in water?

4b What was Margaret Thatcher's maiden name?

5a John Edgar Hoover was the director of which investigative organisation from 1924 to 1972?

5b In the TV programme *The Fall and Rise of Reginald Perrin*, what animal does Reginald visualise when thinking of his mother-in-law?

Answers

1a Horses
1b 1992
2a (Dame) Maggie Smith
2b Exodus
3a *The Searchers*
3b Joanne Kathleen

4a AQ
4b Roberts
5a Federal Bureau of Investigation (accept FBI)
5b Hippopotamus

Player a

Player b

Head to Head

1a What was the name of the first Space Shuttle, launched on 12 April 1981?

1b In Christian tradition, Faith, Hope, Charity, Prudence, Temperance and Fortitude are six of the seven virtues. What is the seventh?

2a Who created the voices for the cartoon characters Porky Pig, Daffy Duck and Bugs Bunny?

2b Which US state has the motto 'North to the Future'?

3a How many cards are there in a regular pack of tarot cards?

3b In Greek mythology, which mountain nymph pined away until only her voice remained?

4a In the 1955 film, who played the character Judy alongside James Dean in *Rebel Without A Cause*?

4b Henry VIII renounced the Pope's authority in 1533 in order to divorce which of his wives?

5a What is the aboriginal name given to Ayers Rock in the Northern Territory, Australia?

5b What is the name of the resort in Wales where the cult TV series *The Prisoner* was filmed?

Answers

1a Columbia	**3b** Echo
1b Justice	**4a** Natalie Wood
2a Mel Blanc	**4b** Catherine of Aragon
2b Alaska	**5a** Uluru
3a 78	**5b** Portmeirion

Player a   1   2   3   4   5

Player b   1   2   3   4   5

1a Which Scottish League football club took its name from the secondary school which its original members attended?

1b According to legend, which game did Sir Francis Drake insist on completing before leaving England to defeat the Spanish Armada?

2a Which controversial 1980s British pop group took their name from an old headline about Frank Sinatra's film plans?

2b The names of how many US states contain the word 'New'?

3a Which two letters represent sodium on the periodic table?

3b Jamie Lee Curtis is the daughter of Tony Curtis and which actress?

4a In mythology, who was the Roman god of fire?

4b Which Eastern European country is also known as White Russia?

5a What is the medical term for short-sightedness?

5b In which American city is the musical *West Side Story* set?

Answers

1a Hamilton Academical
1b Bowls (accept bowling)
2a Frankie Goes To Hollywood
2b Four (Hampshire, Jersey, Mexico and York)
3a Na
3b Janet Leigh

4a Vulcan
4b Belarus (accept Byelorussia/ Republic of Belarus/ Respublika Byelarus)
5a Myopia
5b New York

Player a   1   2   3   4   5

Player b   1   2   3   4   5

Head to Head

1a Which British pop star wrote an autobiography called *Take It Like A Man*?

1b What did the 1923 FA Cup final become known as, after a police horse helped clear large crowds of spectators from the pitch?

2a In Tibetan Buddhism, what name (meaning 'superior one') is given to a spiritual leader?

2b Who was manager of Manchester United when they won the European Cup in 1968?

3a Of which South American country is La Paz the administrative capital?

3b In which sitcom did Robert Lindsay play Wolfie Smith, leader of the Tooting Popular Front?

4a What was the name of the breakaway party started by Sir James Goldsmith which injured the Tories in the 1997 election?

4b What is the title of the senior Church of England clergyman who officiates at the coronation of an English monarch?

5a In theatre, whose plays include *Major Barbara* and *Arms and the Man*?

5b Which term for one-sixth of a circle is also a navigational instrument?

Answers

1a Boy George (accept George O'Dowd)
1b The White Horse Final
2a Lama
2b Sir Matt Busby
3a Bolivia
3b *Citizen Smith*
4a Referendum Party
4b Archbishop of Canterbury (*do not accept just* archbishop)
5a George Bernard Shaw
5b Sextant

 Player a (1) (2) (3) (4) (5)

 Player b (1) (2) (3) (4) (5)

Head to Head

1a Which Shakespeare play features twins separated during a shipwreck?

1b The bronze statue of Hans Christian Andersen's Little Mermaid stands in the entrance to the harbour of which city?

2a In which country was Bianca Jagger, ex-wife of Rolling Stone Mick Jagger, born?

2b What nationality are the papal guard of the Vatican in Rome?

3a In the children's stories, what was the name of Captain Pugwash's ship?

3b Which game show has been hosted by Robin Ray, Robert Robinson and Bob Holness?

4a What was invented by Dr Sylvius in 1650 when he added juniper oil to alcohol in an effort to create a medicine for kidney disorders?

4b Which heart-throb from the silent era of films starred in *The Sheik* and *Blood and Sand*?

5a During which conflict did Brian Hanrahan say (of British aircraft) 'I counted them all out and I counted them all back'?

5b Robert, king of Scotland, beat whose forces at the Battle of Bannockburn?

Answers

1a *Twelfth Night*	**3b** *Call My Bluff*
1b Copenhagen	**4a** Gin
2a Nicaragua	**4b** Rudolph Valentino
2b Swiss	**5a** Falklands Conflict (accept Malvinas)
3a The *Black Pig*	**5b** Edward II

  Player a 1 2 3 4 5

 Player b 1 2 3 4 5

Head to Head

1a In dentistry, what is an alloy of mercury, silver and tin, used to fill tooth cavities?

1b Which member of the British royal family was born at Buckingham Palace in 1960?

2a Which country joined the World War I Allies against Germany in May 1915?

2b In the original stage production of *My Fair Lady*, which actress was the first to play the part of Eliza?

3a The US cities of El Paso and Albuquerque are found on which river?

3b Which future king was invested as Prince of Wales in Caernarvon Castle in 1911?

4a In film, on which planet does the climax of the 1990 film *Total Recall* take place?

4b Name the 20-year-old Russian tennis player who won the September 2000 US Open by beating Pete Sampras in the final.

5a In mythology, Hippolyta was the queen of which female warrior race?

5b In Central America, the Mosquito Coast is on which sea?

Answers

1a Amalgam
1b Prince Andrew (accept Duke of York, Earl of Inverness and Baron Killyleagh)
2a Italy
2b Julie Andrews

3a Rio Grande (accept Rio Bravo)
3b Edward VIII
4a Mars
4b Marat Safin
5a Amazons
5b Caribbean Sea

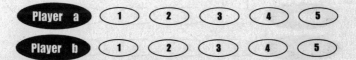

Player a   1   2   3   4   5

Player b   1   2   3   4   5

Head to Head

1a In military history, which German field marshal was nicknamed 'The Desert Fox'?

1b In which English city did balti cooking first become popular in the 1980s?

2a In which area of northern England were Arthur Ransome's *Swallows and Amazons* books mainly set?

2b What is the highest mountain peak in the French Alps?

3a Which patriotic British song comes from *Alfred*, a masque composed by Thomas Arne in 1740?

3b In mythology, when Oedipus blinded himself and left Thebes, which of his daughters acted as his guide until his death?

4a Which Charles Kingsley book, published in 1863, follows Tom the Chimney Sweep who falls into a river and is transformed?

4b Ichtheology is the study of which creatures?

5a The Lord Mayor's Show is traditionally held in the city of London on the second Saturday of which month?

5b Which popular British actress starred with Bill Travers in the 1969 film *Ring of Bright Water*?

Answers

1a Erwin Rommel (accept Rommel)
1b Birmingham
2a Lake District
2b Mont Blanc
3a 'Rule, Britannia!'
3b Antigone
4a *The Water Babies*
4b Fish
5a November
5b Virginia McKenna

Player a 1 2 3 4 5

Player b 1 2 3 4 5

Head to Head

1a In the Jewish religion, for how long does the festival of Hanukkah last?

1b In politics, which former prime minister had a pamphlet published in 1950 called 'One Nation: A Tory Approach to Social Problems'?

2a Which Frank Sinatra song inspired the name of the cartoon character Scooby-Doo?

2b In food, proteins consist of linked chains of which substances?

3a In 1970, Dr Salvador Allende Gossens became president of which country?

3b In medicine, if you have dysphagia, what do you find difficult to do?

4a Which well-known anthropologist said of cities 'The city is not a concrete jungle, it is a human zoo'?

4b In religion, according to St Matthew, Jesus said that 'A prophet is not without honour, save in his own . . .' what?

5a Cleveland bay is a breed of which animal?

5b Which film actor was the most decorated American soldier in World War II?

Answers

1a Eight days (accept eight nights/eight days and nights)	**3b** Swallow
	4a Desmond Morris
1b Sir Edward Heath	**4b** Country (accept land/ house)
2a 'Strangers in the Night'	**5a** Horse
2b Amino acids	**5b** Audie Murphy
3a Chile	

Player a ① ② ③ ④ ⑤

Player b ① ② ③ ④ ⑤

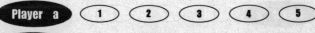

Head to Head

1a Which Welsh fashion designer and manufacturer was born Laura Mountney in Merthyr Tydfil in 1925?

1b Amman is the capital city of which Middle Eastern country?

2a Which unusual medical service began in Australia in 1928?

2b The deficiency of which vitamin causes rickets?

3a Nottingham stands on which river?

3b Who directed the 1971 film *Oh, What a Lovely War!*?

4a In the New Testament, who did Jesus say would inherit the Earth?

4b Dating back to 1912, which Canadian city holds its famous stampede each July?

5a Excluding *Casino Royale* and *Never Say Never Again*, by the end of 1999, how many Bond films had been made?

5b Which member of the cypress family, used to form hedges, can grow three feet in a year?

Answers

1a Laura Ashley
1b Jordan
2a (Royal) Flying Doctor Service (*originally called Aerial Medical Service*)
2b Vitamin D
3a River Trent

3b Sir Richard Attenborough (accept Lord or Baron Attenborough)
4a The meek
4b Calgary
5a 19
5b Leyland cypress (accept leylandii or *Cupressocyparis leylandii*)

Player **a** ① ② ③ ④ ⑤

Player **b** ① ② ③ ④ ⑤

Head to Head

1a In Stephen King's novel of the same name, what was the name of the rabid St Bernard that terrorised the occupants of a farmhouse after being bitten by a bat?

1b By what name was Belize known before 1973?

2a What name is given to an official statement of intended policy issued by a political party?

2b The wigeon is a member of which bird family?

3a Which earl famously appeared on the British Army recruiting posters in World War I?

3b Who was the young female presenter of the 1960s TV show *Ready Steady Go*?

4a Which Irish city's name originates from the Gaelic for 'black pool'?

4b Which composer's film scores include *The Piano* and *The Draughtsman's Contract*?

5a Which ancient Egyptian god, the son of Isis, was often depicted as a falcon-headed man?

5b Which Iraqi-born British businessman and art collector has a gallery in St John's Wood, North London?

Answers

1a Cujo
1b British Honduras
2a Manifesto
2b Duck
3a Kitchener (Earl Horatio Herbert Kitchener of Broome/Baron or Lord Kitchener of Khartoum)

3n Cathy McGowan
4a Dublin (accept Baile Atha Cliath)
4b Michael Nyman
5a Horus
5b Charles Saatchi

 Player a 1 2 3 4 5

Player b 1 2 3 4 5

Head to Head

1a In which 1961 hit song did Elvis Presley sing part of the lyrics in German?

1b What part of the atom did British physicist Sir J. J. Thomson discover in 1897?

2a How many colours can be found on the Bulgarian national flag?

2b Which H. G. Wells novel, published in 1898, describes the arrival of Martians in Woking?

3a In water polo, how many players from a team are allowed in the water at any given time?

3b In nature, what part of the flower is known as the corolla?

4a The Hoare-Laval Pact in 1935 was designed to recognise Italy's invasion of which African country?

4b Which Scottish architect and designer's fame rests primarily on his designs for the Glasgow School of Art between 1897 and 1909?

5a Which city in England is home to the Royal Armouries Museum?

5b What communications material, invented in the 1970s, can carry many thousand times more information than copper wire?

Answers

1a 'Wooden Heart'
1b The electron
2a Three
2b *The War of the Worlds*
3a Seven
3b Petals

4a Abyssinia (accept Ethiopia)
4b Charles Rennie Mackintosh
5a Leeds
5b Fibre optics (accept optical waveguide fibres/fible-optic cable/fibreglass)

Player a   1 2 3 4 5

Player b   1 2 3 4 5

Head to Head

1a Which British pop star played the Goblin King in the 1986 film *Labyrinth*?

1b In British politics, there are three branches of government: the executive, the legislative and the . . . what?

2a In mythology, how many labours were performed by Hercules?

2b In which South American country is the port of Fray Bentos?

3a Which 1943 film co-stars Elizabeth Taylor and a famous collie dog?

3b Which country occupied the Philippines between 1942 and 1945, before the islands became an independent republic in 1946?

4a The dachshund dog was originally bred to hunt which animal?

4b Which 1989 song and video by Madonna was banned by the Vatican and accused of blasphemy, but topped the UK singles chart?

5a What sort of shock is caused by a violent allergic reaction to a substance?

5b In which southern American state did the Bus Boycott in Montgomery take place from 1955 to 1956?

Answers

1a David Bowie
1b Judiciary
2a Twelve
2b Uruguay
3a *Lassie Come Home*
3b Japan

4a Badger
4b 'Like A Prayer'
5a Anaphylactic (shock) (accept anaphylaxis)
5b Alabama

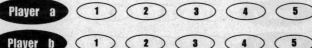

Player a   1   2   3   4   5

Player b   1   2   3   4   5

Head to Head

1a In which US city did Dr Martin Luther King deliver his 'I have a dream' speech?

1b In the animal kingdom, which fish is called a 'smoult' at an early stage in its development?

2a Which instrumental group of the 1960s spent eight weeks at number one in the UK with 'Wonderful Land'?

2b The physicist Heinrich Hertz made discoveries about what type of waves in the 1880s?

3a What is the second largest planet in the solar system?

3b In art, which type of hat features in several paintings by the Surrealist René Magritte?

4a What surname is shared by Trevor and Gerry, who have both been managers of Queen's Park Rangers?

4b In 1969, Hatfield, Sheffield and Sunderland opened the first of what type of learning establishment?

5a The novels of which British prime minister included *Vivian Grey* and *The Young Duke*?

5b The Loop of Henley is found in which organ?

Answers

1a Washington, DC (accept Washington)
1b Salmon
2a The Shadows
2b Radio waves (accept electromagnetic waves)
3a Saturn
3b Bowler hat (accept derby hat)
4a Francis
4b Polytechnics
5a (Benjamin) Disraeli (accept First Earl of Beaconsfield)
5b Kidney

Player a 1 2 3 4 5

Player b 1 2 3 4 5

Head to Head

1a In human biology, nephritis is an inflammation of which part of the body?

1b In literature, which heroine married John Ridd in a book by R. D. Blackmore?

2a In marine biology, how many legs does a crab have, including the pincers?

2b What make of car was designed in Germany in 1934 by Ferdinand Porsche?

3a In pop music, Brian, Carl and Dennis were brothers in the Californian band The Beach Boys. What was their surname?

3b Once Alfred the Great's capital, which English city is also the site of Jane Austen's grave?

4a In sport, how many Olympic gold medals has rower Matthew Pinsent won?

4b The artist Brueghel painted a depiction of the fall of which mythical Greek character?

5a What type of missile was invented by Robert Whitehead at a marine engineering works in modern-day Croatia?

5b In politics, who was the Conservative prime minister from 1963 to 1964?

Answers

1a Kidneys
1b Lorna Doone
2a Ten (accept five pairs)
2b The Volkswagen (accept Beetle/KDF wagon/VW)
3a Wilson
3b Winchester
4a Three
4b Icarus
5a Torpedo
5b (Sir) Alec Douglas-Home

Player a   1   2   3   4   5

Player b   1   2   3   4   5

Head to Head

1a In *Peter Pan*, who was the sister of John and Michael Darling?

1b In which English city was the *Guardian* national newspaper founded in 1821?

2a In netball, how many players on a team are allowed to score?

2b In Roman legend, what was the home city of Aeneas that was destroyed by the Greeks?

3a In politics, which prime minister has served the shortest term since World War II?

3b In the human body, what is synovial fluid produced to lubricate?

4a Cherie Blair's actor father Tony Booth married which former *Coronation Street* star?

4b The Bimini Islands and Eleuthera are part of which island group?

5a Which French underwater explorer was co-inventor of the aqualung?

5b Which bespectacled singer of the 1960s was known as 'The Big O'?

Answers

1a Wendy Darling (accept Wendy)
1b Manchester
2a Two
2b Troy (accept Ilium)
3a Sir Alec Douglas-Home (1963–64) (he served 363 days, just under one year)
3b Joints
4a Pat Phoenix
4b The Bahamas
5a Jacques Cousteau (Jacques Yves Cousteau)
5b Roy Orbison

Player a 1 2 3 4 5

Player b 1 2 3 4 5

Head to Head

1a The actor Sean Bean has a tattoo on his left bicep, referring to which football team?

1b In golf, what is the maximum number of clubs that may be carried during tournament play?

2a Which hymn begins with the line 'And did those feet in ancient time'?

2b In Christianity, 1 November is also known as what day?

3a In the TV comedy series *Only Fools and Horses*, what name did the character of Trigger insist on calling Rodney Trotter?

3b Which chemical element makes up over 70 per cent of the sun?

4a Which city was renamed Ho Chi Minh City in 1976?

4b In music, The Jordanaires were most famously associated with which singer?

5a In the animal kingdom, a spider has a maximum of how many pairs of eyes?

5b In history, who was emperor of Japan between 1926 and 1989?

Answers

1a Sheffield United (Blades) (*do not* accept Sheffield)
1b Fourteen
2a 'Jerusalem'
2b All Saints' Day (accept Hallowmas or All-Hallows)

3a Dave
3b Hydrogen
4a Saigon
4b Elvis Presley
5a Four
5b Hirohito

 Player a   1   2   3   4   5

Player b   1   2   3   4   5

1a In literature, of which gruff animal in Kenneth Grahame's *The Wind in the Willows* does Ratty say 'He simply hates Society'?

1b In Greek legend, which epic poem tells of the wrath of Achilles at the siege of Troy?

2a Which style of hat was made popular by US president Theodore Roosevelt on a tour of Central America in 1906?

2b Which is the largest of the flat fishes?

3a How many stars are there on the Australian flag?

3b Which British astronomer, famous for the comet named after him, devised one of the first practical diving bells in 1717?

4a Do identical twins have the same fingerprints?

4b In religion, in which country was Barbara Harris consecrated as the first female bishop of the Anglican Church?

5a Which Teletubby has a triangle on his head?

5b Who was Home Secretary in 1995 when three prisoners escaped from Parkhurst Prison?

Answers

1a Badger
1b The *Iliad*
2a Panama
2b Halibut (accept Atlantic halibut)
3a Six
3b Edmond Halley

4a No
4b USA (accept America/ United States/US)
5a Tinky Winky
5b Michael Howard

Player a 1 2 3 4 5

Player b 1 2 3 4 5

Head to Head

1a Who wrote the 1939 novel *Finnegans Wake*?

1b What type of creature is a booby?

2a What make of German car was named after the daughter of an Austrian diplomat?

2b What do the letters in the acronym NATO stand for?

3a According to Shakespeare, in *Henry IV Part 2*, 'Uneasy lies the head that wears a . . .' what?

3b What were the ships *Dartmouth*, *Eleanor* and *Beaver* carrying, when their cargo was thrown overboard in Boston in 1773?

4a Which Premier Division football team has fans known as the 'Toon Army'?

4b When journalists Woodward and Bernstein revealed the Watergate scandal, for which paper did they work?

5a In religion, who was the Hebrew leader who succeeded Moses and attacked the walled city of Jericho?

5b In the children's nursery rhyme, who saw Cock Robin die?

Answers

1a James Joyce
1b A bird (large tropical seabird)
2a Mercedes
2b North Atlantic Treaty Organization
3a Crown
3b Tea
4a Newcastle United
4b *Washington Post*
5a Joshua
5b The fly

Head to Head

1a What is the nickname used for the Queen in the satirical magazine *Private Eye*?

1b In television, which BBC drama, starring Gina McKee and Christopher Eccleston, followed four Tyneside friends from the early 1960s through to the mid-1990s?

2a In which German city could you visit the Checkpoint Charlie Museum?

2b How many strings are there on a standard classical guitar?

3a In literature and folklore, which herb is a symbol of remembrance and fidelity?

3b In modern British politics, who is nicknamed 'The Iron Chancellor'?

4a Which of the British Armed Forces is known as the 'Senior Service'?

4b In which European capital city would you find the Cinecitta film studios?

5a What is the seventh colour of the rainbow?

5b A symbol of which religion consists of a star and a crescent moon?

Answers

1a Brenda	**3b** Gordon Brown
1b *Our Friends in the North*	**4a** The Royal Navy (accept Navy)
2a Berlin	**4b** Rome
2b Six	**5a** Violet
3a Rosemary	**5b** Islam

Player a 1 2 3 4 5

Player b 1 2 3 4 5

Head to Head

1a In *The Adventures of Huckleberry Finn*, who is the runaway slave who shares a raft with Huck?

1b Which British novelist wrote *The Forsyte Saga*, published between 1906 and 1931?

2a Who is the only British Prime Minister to have served two non-consecutive terms since 1960?

2b In TV, what was the name of Arthur Lowe's character in the sitcom *Dad's Army*?

3a Which track was released as a double A-side with the Beatles song 'Penny Lane' in 1967?

3b The bulbs of which plant were the subject of a trading mania in seventeenth-century Holland?

4a In the human body, the adjective 'pulmonary' refers to which organ in the body?

4b The 1993 film *Shadowlands*, starring Anthony Hopkins, depicts the love life of which novelist?

5a Which form of transport takes its name from a Japanese term for 'human-powered vehicle'?

5b In which month does the UK's Commonwealth Day fall?

Answers

1a Jim
1b John Galsworthy
2a Harold Wilson
2b Captain Mannering (Captain George Mannering)
3a 'Strawberry Fields Forever'

3b Tulip
4a Lungs
4b C. S. Lewis
5a Rickshaw
5b March

Player a 1 2 3 4 5

Player b 1 2 3 4 5

Head to Head

1a In the children's TV programme *Bagpuss*, what was the name of the girl who brought new items to the shop?

1b Which English medical journal was established by Dr Thomas Wakley in 1823?

2a Which playwright and comedienne is married to the magician Geoffrey Durham, otherwise known as 'The Great Soprendo'?

2b In the animal kingdom, the kea is a parrot found only in which country?

3a In pop music, Jimi Hendrix had a UK hit in 1968 with 'All Along the Watchtower', but who wrote and recorded it originally?

3b In which ocean are the Faroe Islands located?

4a What was the first name of the artist L. S. Lowry?

4b In literature, which surname connects the creators of the characters Sherlock Holmes and Paddy Clarke?

5a In chemistry, what is the first element in the periodic table?

5b By what name is Leslie Townes Hope better known?

Answers

1a Emily	**3b** (North) Atlantic
1b The *Lancet*	**4a** Laurence
2a Victoria Wood	**4b** Doyle (Arthur Conan and Roddy)
2b New Zealand	**5a** Hydrogen
3a Bob Dylan (Robert Allen Zimmerman)	**5b** Bob Hope

Player a   1   2   3   4   5

Player b   1   2   3   4   5

Head to Head

1a In the animal kingdom, the Brown Swiss and Red Sindhi are types of which farm animal?

1b In which year of the 1980s did the Duke and Duchess of York get married?

2a In which month is Saint Swithun's Day?

2b In horse racing, which Grand National winner was named after Alistair, David, Nicola and Timothy, the grandchildren of his breeder, Tommy Barron?

3a In *EastEnders*, the Queen Victoria pub is at the corner of Albert Square and which street?

3b In which European city is the World Trade Organization based?

4a Which British evolutionary biologist wrote the books *The Selfish Gene* and *The Blind Watchmaker*?

4b In Stanley Kubrick's film *A Clockwork Orange*, who was Alex's favourite classical composer?

5a In Greek legend, who was the last king of Troy?

5b In theatre, which play by Tom Stoppard is a comedy based on two minor characters from *Hamlet*?

Answers

1a Cow (accept dairy cattle/ cattle)
1b 1986
2a July (15 July)
2b Aldaniti
3a Bridge Street
3b Geneva

4a Richard Dawkins (Clinton Richard Dawkins)
4b Beethoven (accept Ludwig van Beethoven)
5a Priam
5b *Rosencrantz and Guildenstern are Dead*

Player a (1) (2) (3) (4) (5)

Player b (1) (2) (3) (4) (5)

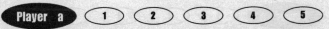

Head to Head

1a By which of her first names was Franklin D. Roosevelt's wife more commonly known?

1b From what was Captain Ahab's artificial leg made in Herman Melville's novel *Moby Dick*?

2a In mythology, what type of animal pulled the Roman god Bacchus's chariot when he entered Thebes?

2b Which famous Irish actor played an aggressive Rugby League player in the 1963 film *This Sporting Life*?

3a What would you collect if you spoke of 'First Day Covers' and 'Cape Triangulars'?

3b In television, which FBI agent's computer password is 'TRUSTNO1'?

4a Dame Trot traditionally appears in which pantomime?

4b What does heliotherapy use to promote healing?

5a Michael Portillo was elected MP for Kensington and Chelsea in 1999 in a by-election following the death of which MP?

5b In football, Everton share their nickname with which type of sweet?

Answers

1a Eleanor
1b Whalebone (accept whale's jawbone/ivory)
2a Elephant(s)
2b Richard Harris (Richard St John Harris)
3a Stamps
3b Fox Mulder
4a *Jack and the Beanstalk*
4b Light (sunlight)
5a Alan Clark
5b Toffee

Player a

Player b

Head to Head

1a In military history, whom did a loblolly boy assist on a ship?

1b In literature, which surname connects the authors of *To Kill A Mockingbird* and *Cider With Rosie*?

2a Which is the only American state to feature the portrait of a president in the centre of its flag?

2b The Peak District National Park lies mainly in which county?

3a In which Irish city are St Stephen's Green and O'Connell Street found?

3b In the animal kingdom, the nurse and the carpet are both species of which fish?

4a Grenadine is a non-alcoholic cordial made from which tropical fruit?

4b What was the nickname of Jimmy Nail's character in the 1980s TV drama series *Auf Wiedersehen, Pet*?

5a Which Hollywood actor appeared as the character Mr Freeze in the 1997 film *Batman and Robin*?

5b In Greek mythology, who was Antigone's father?

Answers

1a Surgeon (accept doctor)	**3b** Shark
1b Lee (Harper and Laurie)	**4a** Pomegranate
2a Washington	**4b** Oz
2b Derbyshire	**5a** Arnold Schwarzenegger
3a Dublin	**5b** Oedipus

Player a   1   2   3   4   5

Player b   1   2   3   4   5

Sudden Death

1a In politics, the Beehive is a parliamentary building in which country?

1b In which 1999 animated film did the characters Slinky and Jessie appear?

2a In which county in north-central England are the Rivers Derwent, Trent, Dove and Rother?

2b A set of British stamps, issued in 1997, commemorated the 450th anniversary of the death of which Tudor king?

3a According to tradition, what is the correct form of address when speaking to the Pope?

3b Which English city was known as Glevum by the Romans?

4a In pop music, which English singer had a hit in 1989 with 'Road to Hell'?

4b In board games, how many blank tiles are there in a standard edition of Scrabble?

5a In what type of geometric design is a tessera found?

5b Which actor played the character Robin Tripp in the TV sitcoms *Man About the House* and *Robin's Nest*?

Answers

1a New Zealand	**3b** Gloucester
1b Toy Story 2 (not Toy Story)	**4a** Chris Rea
2a Derbyshire	**4b** Two
2b Henry VIII	**5a** Mosaic
3a Your Holiness/Most Holy Father	**5b** Richard O'Sullivan

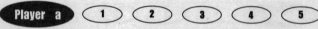

Sudden Death

1a In British history, how many British kings have officially been called Charles?

1b In nature, what colour are the tiny female flowers on a hazel tree?

2a In the animal kingdom, the first cats known to have been domesticated came from which country?

2b In football, which position did Gordon Banks play during his professional career?

3a In the animal kingdom, how is the *Canis familiaris* more commonly known?

3b What biblical name is given to the plant *Polemonium*, because its leaves look like the rungs of a ladder?

4a In *Oliver Twist* by Charles Dickens, what was the name of Bill Sikes's mistress?

4b In pop music, what song title connects the artists Buddy Holly, Steps and Nick Berry?

5a In geography, how many countries share a border with Thailand?

5b Which newspaper comic strip features four children and a large dog called Boot?

Answers

1a Two	**3b** Jacob's Ladder
1b Red	**4a** Nancy
2a Egypt	**4b** 'Heartbeat'
2b Goalkeeper	**5a** Four
3a Dog (domestic dog)	**5b** *The Perishers*

Player a   1   2   3   4   5

Player b   1   2   3   4   5

'WEAKEST LINK'

CONGRATULATIONS!

You can now take the first step towards becoming a contestant on **'WEAKEST LINK'**. All you need to do is fill out this form and send it back to us. Before you start, here are a few points to remember:

- **Please attach a recent photo of yourself (this is non-returnable).**
- **Please write clearly using an ink pen – if we cannot read your details, we won't be able to consider you.**
- **Please ensure that any information you give us about yourself is accurate.**
- **You may photocopy the application form.**

AUDITIONS

Due to the amount of correspondence we receive, unfortunately we cannot acknowledge receipt of application forms. We also cannot audition everyone who applies to the programme. If you are invited to attend an audition we will contact you with details of when and where it will take place.

Please note that guests will **NOT** be permitted to watch the audition session. They will be asked to wait in the reception area.

We regret that we are not able to reimburse travelling expenses to attend the audition, but if you are selected to take part in the show your travel and accommodation expenses for the filming **only** will be covered.

Please return the completed form to:

**WEAKEST LINK
BBC
FREEPOST**

'WEAKEST LINK'
CONTESTANT APPLICATION FORM

TITLE (MR, MRS, MS, MISS): ....

FIRST NAME(S): .... **SURNAME:** ....

ADDRESS: ....

DATE OF BIRTH: .... **AGE:** ....

TEL NOS & CONTACT DETAILS (please include STD Codes):

Day/Work:........................... **Eve/Home:** ....

Mobile: .... **E-mail Address:** ....

Fax: ....

CAN YOU ACCEPT CALLS AT WORK? *YES / NO*

How long have you been resident in the UK? ....

Marital Status: .... **Occupation:** ....

Previous Jobs (please include temporary jobs, student jobs etc.): ....
....
....

Please list six words which best describe you: ....
....

**What other TV shows have you appeared on or been interviewed for
before? (please give name of show and approximate dates)**
....
....

**What types of competitions or quizzes have you won or taken part
in other than television shows?**
....
....

What is your main active hobby or interest? ....

What other hobbies and interests do you have? ....
....

What are your favourite TV programmes & quiz shows? ....

....

If you won the Weakest Link prize money what would you spend it on?

....

How competitive are you? (please give an example)

....

....

Do you regard yourself as a team player? (please give an example)

....

....

Please circle the 3 most convenient locations for audition on the list below, indicating order of preference with a 1, 2 or 3 (1 being the most convenient).

BELFAST	BIRMINGHAM	BRISTOL	CAMBRIDGE
CARDIFF	EDINBURGH	GLASGOW	INVERNESS
LEEDS	LIVERPOOL	LONDON	MANCHESTER
NEWCASTLE	NOTTINGHAM	PLYMOUTH	SHEFFIELD
SOUTHAMPTON	YORK		

Please write here any dates on which you will *not* be available between now and May 2002: ....

....

Do you have an undischarged Criminal Record? *YES / NO*

If YES, please give details ....

I acknowledge that this criminal conviction information may be held on the Weakest Link Contestant Database.

I acknowledge that I am neither a BBC employee or contractor, nor a close relative of a BBC employee or contractor.

I confirm that all information provided on this application form is correct and I agree for it to be held on the Weakest Link Contestant Database until I advise that I no longer wish to be considered as a contestant. If any of the above information changes I will inform the Production Team.

SIGNATURE: .... **DATE:** ....

PLEASE NOTE THAT YOUR APPLICATION CANNOT BE PROCESSED WITHOUT YOUR SIGNATURE TO THE ABOVE CLAUSES.